D1503488

Edited by Carmen Sorrentino

Real-time transcription by Wim Gerbecks

Revised by Simona Benedetti, Cecilia Bevilacqua, Elettra Filardo, Jamie Kowalczyk, Paola Liguori, Gaja Maestri, Francesco Sani, Valentina Angela Stella and Gianfranco Spadaccia

Translated by BRUSSELS LANGUAGE SERVICES sprl/bvba

Translation from Spanish by Caterina Punzo

Translation from French to English by Elis Bertazzon

Designed by Gianluca Lucchese

A special thank you to Lorenzo Lipparini

Remark: not every speaker revised her/his own intervention. For publishing reasons, also revised texts were modified by the editor sometimes. The original video-broadcast version of every speech is available at www.freedomofresearch.org thanks to RadioRadicale.it

WITH THE SUPPORT OF:

Nonviolent Radical Party, transnational, transparty

ALDE Group in the European Parliament

Socialist Group in the European Parliament

Amyotrophic Lateral Sclerosis Liga, Belgium

ESHRE- European Society of Human Reproduction and Embryology

ISEI – Institute for Science Ethics and Innovation, University of Manchester

Proceedings of the Second Meeting of the
WORLD CONGRESS FOR FREEDOM
OF SCIENTIFIC RESEARCH

(European Parliament – Brussels, March 5-7, 2009)

© 2010 – MIMESIS EDIZIONI (Milano – Udine)
www. mimesisedizioni. it / www. mimesisbookshop. com
Via Risorgimento, 33 – 20099 Sesto San Giovanni (MI)
Telefono e fax: +39 02 89403935
E-mail: mimesised@tiscali. it
Via Chiamparis, 94 – 33013 Gemona del Friuli (UD)
E-mail: info. mim@mim-c. net

INDEX

The challenges for reproductive medicine in Europe
(Session proposed by ESHRE - European Society of Human Reproduction)

The religious, bioethical and political approaches to freedom of research

The geopolicy and the future of genetic, regenerative and reproductive medicine

Neuroethics: challenges and opportunities

Fredoom of research between funding, careers and politics

The way ahead: the globlal monitoring on the state of freedom of research and other missions for a permanent World Congress

Proceedings of the Second Meeting of the
WORLD CONGRESS FOR FREEDOM
OF SCIENTIFIC RESEARCH

Introduction

"To the violence of this cynical prohibition on scientific research and on the fundamental rights of citizens, I have responded with my body, which maybe many would have liked to see just as a hopeless prison while today I respond with my thirst for air – because I am truly breathless – which is my thirst for truth, my thirst for freedom". So Luca Coscioni, through his digital vocal synthesizer, opened the first meeting of the World Congress for the Freedom of Scientific Research in February 2006, only days before a respiratory failure cut short his fight for life and against Amyotrophic Lateral Sclerosis.

The Congress had been promoted by Luca Coscioni Association and the Nonviolent Radical Party, transnational and transparty in the summer of 2004 to challenge those who, within the United Nations, intended to ban all forms of cloning, even for therapeutic purposes. Four months of international mobilization, with the support of two American organisations - the Coalition for the Advancement of Medical Research and the Genetics Policy Institute - pre-empted such ban. The proposed ban was turned into a non-binding declaration (backed by eighty UN members, headed by the Holy See), with no effect on national legislation. Luca Coscioni's appeal "against an international ban on human embryonic stem cell research" gathered a total of more than 1,500 signatures from politicians and scientists, including seventy-seven Nobel Prize winners, fifty of whom had previously given their support to Luca's candidacy in the Radical Party's Bonino-Pannella lists during Italy's 2001 election campaign.

The Founding Session of the World Congress was held in autumn 2004 and gathered scientists at the forefront of their field and echoed the one of 1950, when a Congress for Cultural Freedom had been created with the help of some of the most distinguished intellectuals of the time. "On that occasion," writes Gilberto Corbellini, Co-President of Luca Coscioni Association, "some of the most important intellectuals gathered to fight against the fundamentalist and dogmatic cultural manipulations of Stalinist communism".

Since 2004 Luca Coscioni Association was given the role of Operational Secretariat of the Congress, which was created as a permanent forum at the service of scientists, patients, politicians, all true protagonists bound by a common objective: freedom of scientific research throughout the world. From the 16th to the 18th of February 2006, the Protomoteca of Campidoglio in Rome hosted the first gathering of the World Congress, marking the start of a campaign aiming at renewing the EU's funding for human embryonic stem cell research. The initiative had some success within the European Parliament and the European Council, releasing the necessary research funds, although it did not manage to obtain funding for the so-called "therapeutic cloning". The second meeting was held at the European Parliament in Brussels from the 5th to the 7th March 2009, thanks to the central role played by the European Union and by the network that had been put into place. The final declaration of that meeting, subsequently published with the names of the first signatories, is a charter of personal and political commitment to pursue concrete objectives such as: monitoring the freedom of research and healthcare around the world; strengthening policies towards the right to freedom of research; creating an international network in aid of spreading accurate information on access to treatments and of defending patients against violations of their right to safe and effective healthcare; promoting the teaching of the scientific method; asserting an individual's right to self-determination in healthcare matters; putting into practice the UN Declaration on the Rights of People with Disabilities.

Since the meeting, the proceedings of which are in this volume, there have been several initiatives, such as the creation of a fund to safeguard research with human embryonic stem cell research and of an international civic aid network for patients; furthermore, the monitoring of various countries has been put into place, the results of which, along with statements and comments, have been distributed through a monthly newsletter sent out to thousands of politicians and academics worldwide.

The work of the World Congress is in constant development, and the website www.freedomofresearch.org provides regular updates as well as archive search facilities - including the proceedings from previous meetings, in various languages.

We wish to invite the reader to make this work known to others - a work which, in spite of its modest means and resources, contains challenging topics and objectives.

On behalf of Associazione Luca Coscioni,
Marco Cappato and Carmen Sorrentino, Rome, April 2010

Final declaration

We, the undersigned, women and men of science, politicians, citizens met at the headquarters of the European Parliament in Brussels 5-7 March 2009 for the Second meeting of the World Congress for Freedom of Research:

We welcome the continuation of the World Congress initiative, started with the Founding Session meeting in October 2004 and continued through the first meeting in February 2006; those events were decisive for the success of the campaign at the United Nations against the proposal to ban embryonic stem cell research, as well as for the campaign in favour of the financing of such research by the European Union;

With the continuing attacks to free knowledge and research, freedom of conscience and religious freedom from various forms of obscurantism (political-ideological as well as dogmatic-religious), we feel it is urgent and necessary to make further steps towards the consolidation of the World Congress as the permanent forum for discussion and initiative for the human, civil and political rights of every citizen;

In particular, we need to respond systematically and in an organized way to the great social issue of our time: that of disease and disability in an aging population, of the novel possibilities and prospects for cure related to the advances in bio-medical research, as well as the technological instruments and new form of self-managed assistance that increasingly permit recovery of lost faculties and the overcoming of disability. "From the body to the body politic" is a program of action that we propose for today to scientists, patients, politicians and all people of good will.

We, the undersigned, identify the following specific objectives to be pursued at all levels, transnational, national and local:

- monitoring the state of freedom of research and cure in the world, through an annual report, and a constant update of the comparison of laws and national policies;
- strengthening or creation of policies, rules and jurisdictions,

including international and constitutional law to defend the freedom of research, which corresponds to a duty of States to promote free research and to disseminate the benefits of such research in an equitable manner for all citizens (according to Article 15, par. 1(b) and 3 of the International Covenant on Economic, Social and Cultural Rights), including through co-operation with less developed area of the world;
• freedom of research on stem cells, including:
1. overcoming the prohibitions placed by the EU on the eligibility for financing of research obtained by the technique of cell nuclear transfer;
2. overcoming the prohibitions proposed, although in a non-binding document, at the United Nations;
• the creation of an international network to help disseminating accurate information about access to treatment in the world and protecting patients from any violation of the right to a safe and efficacious treatment, an international service of "civil rescue" providing guidelines as the ones prepared by the International Society for Stem Cells Research on clinical translation of stem cell research;
• the promotion of the scientific teaching method, both for its practical value, and for its decisive role in the defence of the democratic method and tolerance;
• the affirmation of the right to self-determination on treatments, according to the principle that no one shall be subjected to treatment against his will, and everyone can decide when and how to begin, continue or discontinue therapy, even in the case that the suspension would lead to death;
• the implementation of the UN Declaration on the Rights of People with Disabilities, in particular in less developed countries.
To organize specific campaigns on the above objectives, we the undersigned:
• Confirm the Association Luca Coscioni's role as Operational Secretariat;
• Is committed to creating networks and working groups bringing together scientists and Nobel laureates, patients, non-governmental, political and institutional representatives, in collaboration with the Nonviolent Radical Party, transnational and transparty (a non-governmental organization with consultative status at the United Nations). *

Brussels, 7 March 2009

LIST OF SIGNATORIES:

Gilberto Corbellini
History of Medicine and Bioethics, University of Rome "Sapienza", Italy; Co-President of Luca Coscioni Association
Paolo De Coppi
MD, PhD, Clinical Senior Lecturer and Consultant, Great Ormond Street Hospital and UCL Institute of Child Health, London, UK
Paolo Di Modica
Musician, affected by ALS
Kathinka Evers
Center for Research Ethics and Bioethics, Uppsala, Sweden
Barbara Forrest
Department of History & Political Science, Southeastern Louisiana University, USA
Gabriela Gebrin Cezar
Assistant Professor, University of Wisconsin-Madison, USA
Alois Gratwohl
Hematology, University Hospital, Basel, Switzerland
Pervez Hoodbhoy
Chairman, Department of Physics, Quaid-e-Azam University, Pakistan
Marisa Jaconi
Department of Pathology and Immunology, Geneva University, Switzerland
Miguel Kottow
Universidad de Chile; Member, Latin American and Caribbean Network for Bioethics of UNESCO
Harold Kroto
Nobel Prize in Chemistry, 1996
Fabio Marazzi
University of Bergamo, Italy
Alex Mauron
Associate Professor of Bioethics, University of Geneva Medical School, Switzerland
Stephen Minger
Director, King's Stem Cell Biology Laboratory, London
Kary Mullis
Nobel Prize in Chemistry, 1993
Martin L. Perl
Nobel Prize in Physics, 1995
Danny Reviers
Chairman of ALS Liga Belgium, affected by ALS

Sir Richard Roberts
Nobel Prize in Physiology or Medicine, 1993
Charles Sabine
NBC News Correspondent
Amedeo Santosuosso
Judge, Milan Court of Appeal, Italy
Miodrag Stojkovic
Centro de Investigacion Principe Felipe, Valencia, Spain
Lord Dick Taverne
Founder, Sense about Science; Member, House of Lords Science and
Technology Committee, United Kingdom
Marco Traub
Transeuropean Stem Cell Therapy Consortium (TESCT),
Switzerland, United Kingdom
Betty Williams
Nobel Prize in Peace, 1970

*the World Congress Secretariat will further explore some of the is-
sues that have emerged during the debate, such as:*
- *the issue of funds for military research and the possibility
  of partially diverting it into research for civilian purposes;*
- *the implications of neurosciences;*
- *the implications of nanotechnologies;*
- *the genetically modified foods;*
- *free access to scientific knowledge.*

Danny Reviers*
Message

First of all sincere thanks to Marco for his beautiful organization of the conference and for giving us the chance to participate. I am happy that we have heard all kinds of statements.
From our organization in Belgium and as member of the international ALS alliance we have daily contact with fatally ill people. For people with ALS - a neurodegenerative disease - who
have hardly three years to live and who received terrible predictions, the choice is easier than for people who are not fatally ill.
We have to grab every legal chance we get to combat such a disease. Every opinion has its own value and everyone decides that
for himself, but when it concerns human lives everyone needs
to surpass his own opinion. We have to clear out together which
type of research for which type of condition is necessary or not;
which one is relevant and has a surplus value or has none;
where and when it deals with abuse and fraud and which research activity to support or not. But never forget that it is about
human lives, many human lives worldwide and patients who always want to decide about their own lives and who are willing
to undergo any test. When is that kind of research relevant to
you or to us? One life can be saved, the other will only be pro-
longed for a short time, everyone has to clear that out for himself. If things do not exist legally, life-threateningly ill people
will search elsewhere and they are often very vulnerable in their
despair. There needs to come more freedom for researchers and
also more financial resources worldwide. Every new research
method has known its own difficulties, this is the same for stem
cell treatments. But I am convinced that today's obstacle will
soon belong to the past.

Marco, I hope that there will be a succession to this conference
and that we will also be involved.

What we need in this situation is more publicity for freedom
of scientific research. What we need are a few important people
with big names like Christopher Reeve and Ronald Reagan were

and like today are Michael J. Fox and Mohammed Ali to give more pressure and to find money. Thank you very much.

*Chairman of ALS Liga Belgium

Opening Ceremony

Marco Cappato*
Opening speech

First of all, let me wish you all a good morning and welcome you to this Second Meeting of the World Congress for Freedom of Scientific Research. To be sure, if we count the Founding Session, this is the third meeting of the World Congress for Freedom of Research.

I shall just make a few introductory remarks and then give the floor to other speakers, since this morning's session is quite important. There will be contributions from European Commissioner Janez Potočnik, former Commissioner Philippe Busquin, Charles Sabine, Nobel laureate Kary Mullis, and we shall also reserve some time for discussion. I can also see some colleagues from the European Parliament here today, such as Paulo Casaca.

We chose this moment and this meeting and venue because I believe that this is first and foremost a crucial time for research and science throughout the world. We are witnessing a genuine qualitative leap, an acceleration in technical and scientific progress, and this acceleration is focusing ever more closely on fundamental questions, such as the genome, the actual structure of the building blocks of life. This amazing qualitative leap, this acceleration in scientific progress is being matched, however, by a gathering of the forces of darkness, the enemy of this kind of progress. The quest for control over the bodies and lives of human beings has always been a feature of the obscurantist forces shaped by religion and dogma as well as politics and ideology.

At the present time this desire for power and influence is braced by a widespread social phenomenon: fear. Faced with the possibility that science may be able to affect the elements which constitute our biological makeup, our DNA, ignorance and poor education often take the form of fear, which is supported by the enemies of knowledge, of freedom of religion and freedom of thought.

We were witnesses of this phenomenon in Italy when, in the wake of the 1970s, the Vatican was defeated in referenda on such matters as divorce and abortion, and in the most recent referendum of a few years ago, dealing with scientific research, the embryo and in vitro fertilisation, when the strategy adopted by our adversaries was not that of striving to win, but of persuading the Italian people not to vote, so effectively playing on their fear and lack of information that they were successful. In Italy, as you know, for a referendum to be valid 50% plus one of the people must vote, and the outcome was that it was impossible to change the law on IVF.

Fear, however, can be fought with information, knowledge and education on scientific method, one of the fundamental elements in our democracy. Scientific method has introduced the principle of fallibility, the possibility of error, the need to test in real terms the search for the truth, truth with a lower-case 't', the truth that we need in our everyday lives as a hedge against absolutism, that is the dogma of revealed Truth, Truth with a capital 'T', the kind of truth that is never subjected, nor ever can be, to the possibility of error or to testing.

But this is not all. Fear of research and science is also in many cases the result of social inequalities, particularly in respect of access to the benefits of research and science. Scientific research alleviates some ethical problem areas, but the real ethical problem is that of accessibility by the greater number of individuals to the benefits of this research. The fact is that at the present time the greater part of the population of the world is excluded from those benefits. The issue of rules and policies is therefore another task to be shouldered in the matter of spreading the benefits of research. This is also due to the fact that while ethics affects access to treatments, medicines and therapies, it may also concern the genome, DNA, as is indeed the case to a certain degree, so that the problem is all the more persistent. Discrimination and inequality tend to be all the more exaggerated because we are witnessing the appearance of genuine anthropological differences between those who have access to a certain type of treatment and those who have not.

When we speak of research and science, we should be aware that it is the future of democracy which is at stake, because life - how it starts and how it ends - are the processes which the enemies of science would like to hold as sacred, as questions which should be seen as absolutes, in which the State, the Government, the law and, indeed, democracy itself, have no place. Accepting this kind of imposition is very dangerous because life, health, the beginning and end of life are increasingly being seen as processes which we can indeed affect. We are being provided with an increasing number of tools to help us making our own decisions, decisions about how we shall be treated and how we shall access the benefits of science.

If our democracies refuse to control these processes, they will end up being controlled by other powers, probably dictatorial or tech-nocratic powers which are not concerned with the problems of democracy or accountability, with the responsibility of being an-swerable to the people. If we take a look at what is happening in many countries around the world, the results of our bans - such as that on stem cell research - are desperate journeys to countries which pretend to have cures, which in reality do not exist. The failure to control these processes therefore stands as one of our most heavy responsibilities, because there will always be others, outside democ-racy and the law, who will strive to do so. Science and research are in danger of losing their strength if not backed by the consensus of the people. This means that education, information and democratic debate are crucial for the future of research.

We began this World Congress, this journey, four years ago, and we did so thanks to the leadership of Luca Coscioni. Our interna-tional guests are probably unaware of this, but when we were re-quired to select our governing elements through the internet, Luca Coscioni wrote an email to the Radical Party. At that time we were unacquainted with this victim of Amyotrophic Lateral Sclerosis, writ-ing to say that he wished to take part in these elections in order to fight for the freedom to carry out embryonic stem cell research, one of the few hopes for conditions such as. Several months later, he be-came the President of the Italian Radicals, the leading candidate from our movement, and as such he was supported by 50 Nobel lau-reates, backing not only the victim of that disease, but also the indi-vidual who was taking the responsibility to make use of his weakness, his extreme weakness, as an element which all who be-lieve in the urgency of the need for freedom of research and thought could benefit by.

It was on the basis of this campaign that the first mobilisation on an international scale arose when the Vatican, along with Italy and several other countries, sought to get the United Nations to pass a resolution banning any form of cloning, including cloning for ther-apeutic purposes. The cloning, however, turned out to be an inter-national movement, when dozens of Nobel laureates managed to block that attempt. The UN did pass a declaration, but it was not legally binding.

Subsequently, before the first meeting of the World Congress, we started another battle, one for the donation of European funds - through the Seventh Framework Programme, initiated by Philippe Busquin - on stem cell research, any kind of stem cells, with no dis-crimination against embryonic stem cells. And in this case, too, with the support of parliamentarians, of the Honourable Véronique De

Keyser, who is here today and to whom we raise our hats, and of the patients' organisations, we managed to achieve a successful result.

Luca Coscioni died two days after the first meeting of our World Congress, but our work and the struggle continue. We shall use these three working days we have ahead of us to analyse the theoretical, academic, philosophical and even religious implications of freedom of research, and to discuss the urgent initiatives we can take together: scientists, Nobel laureates, political representatives, ministers, victims of disability or disease, and associations. I say together because - as our motto states: "From the body to the body politic" - it is our wish that the subjects discussed here should not be seen as marginal from the political viewpoint, but rather as aspects of the great social issue of disease and disability, and with the extension of the average human lifespan and a greater possibility for each individual to make his own decisions about his own fate, this ever more important social issue becomes a political issue.

We intend to set a series of objectives for the discussion, within the framework of the UN, of the European Union, or of the individual international situations, which concern freedom to carry out research, funding, the monitoring of the legislative situation, and the freedom for research to be entrusted to the researchers. Other matters will also be addressed, such as teaching the scientific method and the creationism/evolutionism problem, as well as other proposals which have already been outlined in the pre-Congress documentation, such as that of the reallocation of military funding for research to benefit the health of the people.

This is a congress, an open debate, but the important factor is that this Congress is not a unique event. We would like to see it become a permanent forum for working together, and for this reason, we are all the more grateful for your presence here, at the European Parliament.

*MEP;
Secretary General, Luca Coscioni Association

Janez Potočnik*
**The role of the European Union
for freedom of scientific research**

It is an interesting time we live in. It is an interesting topic, your conference is addressing. There are certain lessons which could be also learned from the financial crisis, but let us focus on science. Freedom and freedom of scientific research are such powerful concepts, so interesting in our humanity.

As some of you probably know, I grew up in former Yugoslavia. I witnessed a brief war that resulted in Slovenian independence and was closely involved in the succession to the European Union. Even if it lasted for a couple of days, I will always remember the transition I went through. It reshuffled my personal situation, to be honest, through my understanding of the most basic human values, as well as through my education and my involvement in society. I promised myself that I would be a good guy till the end of my life.

We all want the freedom to live as we please. We are social human beings. Most of us live in close proximity to others. Freedom as an ideal is necessary in practice. In civilized society the concept of freedom means that one person's freedom should not take away the freedom of his neighbor. A balance needs to be struck between negative and positive types of freedom. Negative freedom means the lack of restraints on actions by any particular individual or entity; positive freedom means having a general framework which preserves freedom for all. Winston Churchill's famous line - "democracy is the worst form of government, except for the all other that have been tried" captures this in a nutshell: by definition, in a democracy we cannot all have everything the way we want it. There is a balance between our obligations and our freedoms. Finding the proper balance is one of the major roles of politics and democratic debate.

Of course our time, with new developments or new understandings, can shift the balance, sometimes gradually, sometimes quite suddenly. Our time's general views of science have changed a lot as well. For much of early history, science and research were seen much more as a danger to established belief systems than a benefit for humankind itself or to the planet as a whole. In modern society, we can look back at this kind of repression, self-evidently wrong, not just on ethical grounds of freedom, but in the sense that it has delayed the scientific progress through which science improves our lives. Today, the general concept of academic freedom is part of our society's framework. Scientific thinking, the freedom of ideas and the idea of knowledge as essential commodity is protected from repression. But science has moved on, too. And the more it helps us understanding the world we live in, the more options it gives to change it. Science, and the technology it helps creating, have expanded human options. We can fly around the world in less than a day. We can instantly connect via the internet. We can treat or prevent most diseases and we work hard on those that continue to threaten us. Research and development are now embedded in the economic systems. They are the engine that drive forward productivity and growth economies. That is widely acknowledged. These are some of the many life-changing and empowering good things science has brought to us. During the last century, the creation and use of the first atomic bomb, just to mention one example, brought home the fact that there were also less noble technologies. For the first time in history, scientific progress has developed to the point to make it possible to imagine mankind destroying itself and the planet we live on. Later in the century we realized the damage we humans were doing and did to the planet. The fragility of nature, and of the planet we depend on, was revealed.

I come to my point: scientific progress has extended the range of human actions. The need for political view has also grown. We have now entered more complicated areas of scientific development. The ones concerning technology have already been mentioned. New questions have been raised about the human and non-human life, cloning, genetic modification, human existence and are mostly minute-level. These advances have spurt on the development of ethical assessment of science. At the EU level we place great emphasis on the ethical dimension: all projects must be conducted in accordance with the EU Charter of Fundamental Rights. Ethical assessment may not always involve legal rules, but may reflect the value system. The European Commission - in active dialogue with other organizations - is committed to help responsible global government on research ethics. However, the general public expects us politicians to protect them from science that they fear sometimes. It may be rational or irrational, but it can still be real. We must make sure that the divide does not emerge between scientists and non-scientists, because it may cause problems to the scientific development. It is not just about needing information or asking permission. We need to truly engage non-scientists in big scientific questions to make sure that they understand and fully contribute. Fear has often been born from my ignorance. Scientists should be active. They have knowledge and responsibility and the public trusts them more than us politicians and the journalists - Europe as a matter of fact and figures do clearly confirm that.

A specific field of scientific research is basic research, that is research driven by one's own curiosity, whose goal is discovering the unexpected and this can lead to new products or new innovations. For instance the discovery of the so-called "buckyballs" was an unexpected by-product of experiments to reproduce molecular formation in interstellar space. The accidental discovery of this special form of carbon lead to the development of carbon nanotubes, a lighter building block in nanoengineering.

I started by saying: freedom and freedom of scientific research are such powerful concepts. So intrinsic to our humanity. We should never forget that, and we should always stand for these principles. I believe in the pragmatic approach, that is the one, which on sensitive issues balances absolute freedom of research with wider common interests. One which establishes effective and appropriate governance. One which is sensible enough to treat each issue on each individual matter and one which is able to involve society. I believe in free and responsible science. I thank you for your attention and wish this conference the very best for the benefit of this very science and for the best of our humanity.

*European Commissioner for Science and Research

Charles Sabine*
A layman's perspective

First of all, there is something I must make clear. That is, I am most certainly not a scientist. So forgive me, if my views and theories are not backed up by data. That is the happy prerogative of the lay social commentator - or, dare I say, *politician* - to be able to cherry pick random areas of debate and pontificate without substantial evidence.

I have spent more than half my life working for NBC News, mostly in places like Gaza, places where conflict is shown as a natural state for men – a need for a stated enemy passed down through generations. Places where the dangers of religious dogma are written in blood. Where the excuse for war may usually be religion, but is, in fact, all about power, and fear forging ethnic or tribal divisions that manifest themselves century after century in cycles of violence. It is a job that has carried me through a kaleidoscope of events. Allowing me to witness many of the most important moments of the last quarter of a century first hand. To see the human spirit at it is most tested. And to draw lessons from those experiences.

In recent years, much of my life has been spent in Baghdad, a place that reminds you that good health can never be taken for granted. That life can throw at you all sorts of things you could do without... often when you are not expecting them.

When my mother gave us news of my father John, from that moment, every single action, performed by every one of us, every single day, would be coloured by that news: he was suffering from Huntington's disease – a condition I, like most people, had never heard of. It was, I was told, incurable – untreatable. And, more than that, genetic. I had a 50/50 chance of having the faulty gene that caused the disease, and if so, the disease would most likely develop in me in the next ten to fifteen years. My first reaction was incredulity. I had spent my working life immersed in the misery that nature, as well as men, can inflict on the human race. But it had never occurred to me my family could be a victim. Then, as the re-

32

ality of the news began to sink in, I could feel the independence, I had spent so long cultivating, fall away like a silk cape from my shoulders, leaving me with a vulnerability and fragility I had not known in adult life.

My father was a career soldier with extra-ordinary humanity. It inspired my mother to insist on nursing him personally till his death. The only battle of his life he lost, was with the dehumanisation of Huntington's. The problem with trying to describe the horror of this disease is that you run out of superlatives in portraying what is worst about it. You might think that dying with a tube down your throat acting for your stomach because it can no longer process food would be the worst thing imaginable. No. Far worse is the loss of dignity that comes for a once proud man to watch friends and family wince as his body and mind become twisted till unrecognisable – as a soul inside lets out a cry for help that no one can hear and weeps a tear that no one can see. But even that is not the worst. No. I know for certain my father would have willingly suffered all of that a hundredfold, if he could have been spared the worst pain by far, which was to know he could pass that nightmare on to his sons. My brother John is five years older than me. He studied law at Oxford and joined one of the most prestigious law firms in Britain. Now, before meeting his neurologist, he practices walking in a straight line because he knows she will ask him to do it, and it is very difficult for him.

My profession has exposed me to an unnaturally large number of dead and injured people. more than a dozen wars, four earthquakes, and more suicide bombings than I can count have left me with more visions of death than anyone would wish for. And that affects your priorities as well as your perspective. I learnt, for example, that the most valuable human quality, is humility. Because none of us is immune from disease or disaster, and we are all the same flesh and bone. In the weeks following the tsunami in South East Asia three years ago, I spent many days at the temples along the coast of Thailand where thousands of bodies were laid out for identification. Now I do not want to go into too much detail about what happens to a body after a week in tropical heat. But suffice to say one result was that we, and the forensic scientists, and even the relatives of the victims, knew that among those bodies were both poor fishermen from the Andaman coast as well as wealthy businessmen from London, or Stockholm, but I swear to you, none of us could tell one from the other. Do not think that because you may now have good health, that research into diseases like that which has struck my family, is not relevant to you. The families whose lives are destroyed by dementia, represent a community hidden by its own shame, and made transparent by a vacuum of self-esteem – but a community far larger than people realise. Think of this – right now 127 million Europeans have one or more brain disorder, costing our health services, by the way, 400 billion euro a year. By middle of the century, it is reckoned that as much as half the population of Europe will have some form of dementia when they die. Most of them, of course, will come from the one-third of the population who will then be over 65. That statistic includes, by the way, anyone in this auditorium still alive then, who is now over the age of 24.

Now, 25 years of watching men kill each other – and it is always men, by the way - has taught me another truth about them. That is, that human beings lose their moral compass, their social equilibrium, if you like, when you take two things away from them: dignity and hope. Now I think we have already shown the vacuum of dignity that those suffering dementia feel. But what about hope? Do they have it? Well, the answer to that lies in the hands of the legislatures, executives and other people who have a say in the way our societies treat the infirm in the 21st century. Because, yes, we could be at a pivotal moment in medical history. The disease that has destroyed my family, for example, may hold the answers to many questions of the future for all of you. Because it can be predicted genetically before it becomes symptomatic. In the future, it is possible that most other diseases could also be predicted through genetic mutations, and treated pre-emptively. Just last month, trials of gene therapy with HIV patients were described by scientists at the University of California as 'exciting' and 'highly promising'. Those trials involved modified stem cells, a field at the threshold of untold promise – a fact recognized by the new US administration, which has already shown its intent to repeal archaic legislation. So, what stands in the way of this historic chapter in medicine being embraced? Well, the two strands of society that usually interweave into a tapestry of blindness – fear and lack of communication. Let's start with the stem cell debate. Here I want to refer to a man whose 200th birthday was celebrated just last month. Charles Darwin's *Origin of the species*, the foundation of biology, was, of course, dismissed by the Church as heresy when it was published 150 years ago. Last September, the Anglican Church apologised to Darwin, quote, "for misunderstanding you, and by getting our first reaction wrong, encouraging others to misunderstand you still". There could be something to be said for suggesting that religious zealots should stay quiet on a subject it will take them a century and a half to understand. But then, as Darwin himself said: "Ignorance more frequently begets confidence than does knowledge. It is those who know little, not those who know much, who so positively assert that a problem will never be solved by science". The Catholic Church has been less ready to apologise to Darwin, the Church that derided Darwin for "insulting the dignity of the human species", the same Church that refused to criticise slavery until 20 years after Darwin's death, a man who had spent his life detesting and campaigning against what he saw as a real crime against human dignity.

Prejudice, you see, is usually born out of fear of the unknown and on the other side of that coin, communication leads to understanding, and understanding dilutes fear. The vacuum left by fear can be filled with hope. I spent many months in the anti-apartheid battles of South Africa in the 1980's and then during Nelson Mandela's release and the first democratic election that followed. In 1996, I was in Cape Town for the start of the Truth and Reconciliation Commission – with its chairman, Archbishop Desmond Tutu. He was appalled at what was uncovered at that commission's two-year investigation but he also described what happened there as a "vision of hope for our time". Over in Northern Ireland, it was that whole South African peace process, according to the IRA, that provided the template for the peace process there. And you know what? Last September, Iraqi leaders met secretly in Finland with delegations from the National Party and ANC from South Africa, and from the IRA and Unionists in Northern Ireland to learn from them how to move a peace process forward. Teamwork - and communication.

So how do we apply that lesson to improving care for the less fortunate among us? Well, one way is to understand more fully, that their needs go beyond anti-depressants. We must, for example, re-define our attitude toward mental illnesses, so that the millions who suffer, can come out from the shadows. Many people at risk of developing Huntington's disease, are not available for essential clinical trials of compounds that may be able to treat the symptoms of my disease. Why? Because, not only do they naturally fear the outcome of a test, but they also fear the repercussions from other people or organizations being privy to that information. Legislatures must protect the rights of these people, in order to give them reassurance. We must do everything we can, to remove the reason why they put off the test, and, incidentally why I did. Fear.

I have learnt to recognise fear – I have seen it more times than I wished on the faces of people about to die, and I have felt it myself. In March 1996, in the last days of the war in Yugoslavia, I was captured with a camera crew by a renegade platoon of Mujahideen guerillas. We were very unfortunately driven into a clearing in the so-called 'Doboi pocket', where they had made their camp. As the sun set and the Mujahideen began a call to prayer, they fired a salvo of missiles at the Serbian lines that were two miles to the North. I was by the door of our armoured car and could see the blood splattered wall where two overseas development workers had been blindfolded and shot the day before. The young fighter who had held an AK 47 to my chest for the last five hours, took the pin out of a grenade which he then held to my head while he closed his eyes and prayed to Allah. That is an experience of real fear. But not that moment, nor any other I have experienced, in-stills more fear, dread, and terror, as Huntington's disease in the end, though, I did take that test. And discovered that the disease that took my father and is now inflicting on my brother the same terrible decline in his prime, will take me, as well. So three years on from my test, is it any easier? I wished it was. I am utterly terrified. Not an hour goes by, when I do not picture how my quality of life will drain away, question how I will afford care, fear that however much my friends might now promise they will always come and see me, that they won't really want to – just like I did not want to see my father when he lost the ability to converse with me. Every time I take the dogs for a walk, I wonder if this will be the time I realise my coordination has started to fade? And will I be able to dance with my baby daughter on her 16th birthday? That time bomb is real, present, and desperate for all of us who know we have a disease like Huntington's, Alzheimer's or Parkinson's.

Every day, thousands of European men, women, and children slip into the cauldron of despair which is that point where there's no longer the hope that the research of scientists, like those here, might bear fruit in time for them. It is our duty to do everything we can, to improve communication and access to information among those researchers. You do not have to be a scientist to work out that if all laboratories, and indeed individuals, working separately on finding treatments for disease around the world can have access to each other's information the whole of their efforts will be much greater than the sum of the parts. We in Europe should follow the example of the public library of science in the US. The Open Access model gives unrestricted, free distribution, allowing, say, the findings of a researcher here in Brussels, to be accessed freely by a scientist in Beijing. Scientific importance, not profitability, is the sole consideration for publication. But we also need public access hubs, that would also allow families access to information about scientific developments, without having to pay hundreds of dollars to scientific publishers. Of course, we will also need to find a way to make these highly complex scientific matters accessible to ordinary people like me. Not easy, but, with the right application it can be done. We must demystify the science, to engage the families and the scientists together, a communication that will dilute fear, encourage participation, and convey to families, hope. Do not underestimate what the work of the scientists and researchers means to the millions around the world who suffer from these diseases, and the even greater number who care for them, as we scour the newspapers and internet for any fragment of news from their laboratories. Scientists are understandably wary of raising false hopes, but understand, that in a world of total darkness, the very faintest glimmer of light emboldens the human spirit to go on. We must also allow these scientists the right to make mistakes. As Niels Bohr said: "An expert is someone who has made all the mistakes that can be made, but in a very narrow field". And, I would add to that, a great expert is one with the courage and wisdom to know that mistakes have to be made, and used to climb upward, like broken bricks piled against a wall. Now what else might stand in the way of hope? What about funding? Will the shockwaves felt by economies round the world stand in the way of progress? I believe not. In the years during and after the American great depression, creative talent in the USA grew as in no other period in the last century. As great minds turned away from the financial institutions, that were on their knees, and focused on more noble goals. It was the golden age of design. And a new breed of scientists were led by Albert Einstein with the mantra that we cannot solve problems by using the same kind of thinking we used when we created them. That, in his words, "a man's ethical behaviour should be based on sympathy, education and social ties, not religion". You see, you might think that people suffering material losses may be less inclined to prioritise the less fortunate among them. My experience is the opposite. Affluent societies tend to get distracted by the more material matters – cars, gadgets, how much their house is worth. When they are reminded of the relativity of all that, and the fickleness of it all, they tend to focus once more on the more constant priorities of life – family, friendship, health, love, dignity. In the immediate aftermath of the invasion of Iraq in 2003 - when the vacuum of order was filled with unspeakable atrocities – I went to find out what had happened to the country's mentally ill during the war. Now when I left that fly and disease infested bedlam, my first reaction was to think that the words 'God-forsaken' could never have been more apt. But on reflection, I realised that in fact someone's God could not have been more manifested than in the power of human courage and simple love and goodness that nurses showed. It is in the darkest moments that the greatest qualities of the human spirit shine, and in doing so, they give us all hope. It is in the nature of human beings, especially women, to care for the infirm and strive to make them better. No single body – political or religious - has the right to impede that instinct. Not just for the sake of the victim, but for the carer or clinician or physician or scientist. There is of course the argument that all science is relative anyhow, and why not, just save resources from caring for the sick and let God, or natural selection, sort them out. If the Nazis had won the war, I would not be standing here, because they advocated euthanasia for people with my disease. A 1938 poster – a splendid piece of propaganda for the Nazi compulsory euthanasia programme - shows a doctor with a man with Huntington's and the words: "This person suffering from hereditary defects costs the community 60,000 Reichsmark during his lifetime. Fellow Germans, that is your money, too" but this eugenic interpretation of Darwin's theories would have the old boy rolling in his grave. In fact, he was very clear on this issue. The balance of dependency, he said, is part of our social axis, allowing the growth of the instinct of sympathy, which he called "the noblest part of our nature". He would have been very proud of those trying to find a treatment for my disease. Huntington's has had the almost unique power to challenge the human spirit, because of its terrible paradoxical mix of finality and perpetuity. Finality for its individual victims, and perpetuity for the misery it imparts on a family. But the greatest evil has been the way in which it sucks hope into a vortex. But it has not defeated that human spirit, because the very best of humanity surrounds it. I have seen those qualities in the people I have come into contact with around the world who are part of this battle. It is why I am standing here now: the superhuman patience and tirelessness of the families and other carers and the extra-ordinary devotion from the scientists and clinicians that surpasses all logic.

In the last century, Winston Churchill said that a society should be judged by how it treats its prisoners. In the 21st century, I believe, societies will be judged by how they treat their mentally ill. Any person, or organisation, that stands in the way of those who might offer better quality of life, will have their conscience to reckon with. And I pray for their sake, that neither they nor anyone in their family suffers from one of the ailments whose treatments they impede. If their path is clear, it is within the reach of today's scientists to change what is perceived as unchangeable, because the human spirit is capable of anything. In 1991, after the Gulf war that did not remove Saddam, I went to the Iranian border with Iraq after rumors that Kurdish refugees were spilling across it. What we found was a sea of humanity pouring over the mountains, a million people – mostly women and children - running from Saddam's chemical attacks in the North of Iraq. It was winter - bitterly cold and the sights would never have been believed, had there not been a cameraman with me to record them. But the image imprinted in my mind till the day I die was one particular girl of about 12, she was clambering over the rocks, focused on survival, her face dripping with freezing mud, on her back, her younger sister, three or four years old, unconscious and barely alive. She had carried that child almost ninety miles. All humans are capable of far more than you can ever believe.

For brilliant people like those scientists in this hall, a better world created by a vision of hope really is within reach. It may be too late for me, but on behalf of today's children, those who have not been born, and those whose lot it will be to care, for them I say to you: if ever this body – the largest transnational electorate on Earth – had a moral responsibility, it is to allow them the freedom to give the millions who have till now made up a lost European community, dignity and hope. To use the words of President Obama: "Hope – hope in the face of difficulty, hope in the face of uncertainty, the audacity of hope! In the end that is God's greatest gift to us. A belief in things not seen. A belief that there are better days ahead".

*NBC News Correspondent

Kary Mullis*
Scientific progress is a rocky road

I think that, what I will try to do, without being too academic and boring, is to explain something that I feel like is essentially missing in the definition of science.

What I think is really essential, to any kind of legislative understanding of how to deal with science, is to make a big distinction in your mind between what is science and what is technology. Because it is technology that, in fact, concerns people. It is technology that concerns most people in the world, rather than science. Science is something that is practiced only by a very few of us. There are not many real scientists in the world. Most of the people in the world who are considered to be scientists are technologists. What they are doing is making things. They are designing things that have a very real effect on you. They are the doctors who are doctoring you and fixing you when you are broken. They are not scientists. Scientists are a kind of an odd lot of which I consider myself to be one. Scientists are like mathematicians, in the sense that they practice something different from technology. A lot of technology results from what they do. And therefore they are allowed to do it and are paid to do it. But they do not do technology. They are not the people responsible for applying what it is that they do. They do not shoot the guns that kill people. They make the bombs, but they do not drop them. They are the people who design the concepts. The idea of policing a scientist is an empty idea. Scientists do not care what people think. What they write on little pieces of paper or on blackboards is far different from something you will come into contact. I will bring concrete examples to make sense out of it. We heard from Charles (Sabine) that Darwin was a scientist. That he got in trouble with the Church. That was only reasonable. Charles Darwin was a scientist. He was not a technologist. He was not doing anything with evolution. He was not an animal breeder. He was a scientist. The idea that there was something like evolution, nobody but the Church should have been concerned with. It was a scientific idea. Before him, think about Copernicus. What did he do? He was thought of a scientist. He was not a technologist. What he did irritated the Church, but it should not have irritated the average person. He is the person who said: "The Earth turns, the Sun does not go around the Earth". Now, as an example of why that does not really matter to your life, you still consider that the Sun goes around the Earth in your language. We say: "The Sun is coming up". We do not say: "The Earth is turning towards the Sun". The scientific principles are usually no concern to you at all. You can do without them and carry on your life with the fiction that the Sun did in fact rotate around the Earth along with the Moon and Mars. It might matter if you are a technologist and you plan a trip to Mars by rocket. But, the science that led Copernicus and Galileo and others is harmless. It is as harmless as art and obscure mathematics. When scientists decide to write equations to each other, we do not say: that is dangerous stuff. It should be controlled.

It is very different, however, when someone looks at what it means and says: "You know what we could do? We could make a bomb that would be bigger and brighter and stronger than anything else". We better do it quietly, like at Los Alamos, since we do not want anyone to know we are doing it. This is totally different and something that legislative bodies and all humans have a very deep interest in. When scientific knowledge is used in order to cure diseases or to prolong lives, that is of interest to humans. Something they do need to be notified of and they do deserve to have a say on what happens.

But academic matters, as in the question: "How does the heart circulate fluid?" are useless to the average person's issues. This is more the definition of what scientists do, along with mathematicians and astrophysicists. You do not know of any astrophysicists who have discovered anything that will be of interest to you. Most of the things they talk about are so far away from you, you will never even see them, unless you happen to look at a photographic plate made by the Hubble telescope. That is science.

I am not trying to excuse technology. I am saying that if you want to have an effect on the kinds of things that science leads to, make that distinction clear in your mind. There is nothing you need to do about science. What concerns you has to do with technology and the commercial application of science. For instance, the first time I spoke to this body was about four or five years ago. I spoke about genetically modified foods, which I thought of as being interesting. I was rather naïve to think that this body would look at that as being science instead of technology. I did not think about the difference. I did not think of GM foods necessarily as something we should apply everywhere or that we should drop all of the normal food stuff and start using modified food. I was conveying the idea and that it was interesting. In fact, we had been modifying foods in a way for 10,000 years. We had done this not only with our food, but the animals that we raise and by selection, modifying ourselves and offspring. That was the message. It was not to suggest that we do anything different, but just to say that it is true. The concept came from experiments done by the Food and Drug Administration in 1959, in which a great number of seedlings were irradiated by gamma rays. No one at the time understood what DNA was and what they were doing when they radiated the seedlings. They selected the ones they liked and from those experiments, we now have a variety of wheat, with properties that the farmers like. That is an example of technology rather than science. If anybody was against the use of that kind of knowledge, they should look to technology rather than science. There is a big difference.

If you want to mount an effective campaign against the misuse or unequal availability of scientific information, then think about the technology. It was interesting to me when Charles (Sabine) talked about the PLoS, the Public Library of Science, available to all. All scientific knowledge should be put in the hands of anyone, by way of the internet. I think that is the right thing to do. It does not mean it could all be used reasonably, to do anything they want to do with it, by anybody. To know something, or to have access to it, is one thing, but to do something about it is another. To build a factory that is devoted to make weapons like SARIN gas is very different from generating a tiny amount of SARIN gas in a chemistry laboratory because you are interested in compounds of chlorine and carbon. That is science.

There is no reason why any normal human being should be against science. It is like art or mathematics, by itself, it does not cause any harm. To try to control it by saying that we do not like the uses of it, and therefore we are going to stop the acquisition, is wasted effort. It has nothing to do with your ultimate goal which is to have a reasonably equal distribution of the uses of science. One of the great philosophers of science, in my opinion, was Douglas Adams. He wrote the *Hitchhiker's Guide to the Galaxy*. Adams said something in that book that I think captures the essence of what science really is. He said there is a theory which states that if anyone discovers what the universe is for and why it is here, it will immediately disappear and be replaced by something even more bizarre and explicable. That, I think, is funny. But it encapsulates the uselessness of science by itself. Who would care if it were true or not? Who would notice it? That would change science. And science changes all the time. It is not science itself that is of interest to you. It is the uses of it.

There are times when science is immediately publicized by the press, and the worst kinds of science end up in the newspapers. There are consequences when people develop concepts based on that sort of thing. Pellagra is a good example of what I am talking about, and it happened in the State where I was born, around 1916. At that time, people were dependent on corn as a source of carbohydrates for their nutritional needs. In the South of the US, corn grew quite well, compared to wheat or any other grains, so everybody grew corn to eat. What the Southern people did not know was that the Mesoamericans, from Mexico, also used corn as their source of carbohydrate, but they did something strange to it. I do not know how they discovered this, but they took the corn from the cob and soaked it in lye, then dried it and ground it before they ate it. That had the effect of extracting the vitamin B from the husk of the corn, and therefore they could survive on it by itself. When the European settlers discovered how easy it was to grow corn, they did not know to soak it in lye, but just ate it without treating it first. They started developing pellagra, a slowly developing disease which causes changes in your body and kills you eventually. The US government, noticing there was a plague of pellagra in the Southeast, sent a lot of scientists to try and solve this disease. They noticed this disease ran in families. The father got it, the mother usually got it, and the kids would get it. They assumed, an incorrect scientific presumption, that pellagra was contagious and infectious. They thought there was some micro-organism associated with the house that caused the disease to progress from parents to children. Their solution was to take the children out of the homes and put them in orphanages. An enormous number of children were removed from their houses in the Southeast and put into orphanages. While there, the children were given normal bread and of course, got better.

Finally a doctor, Joseph Goldberger, was sent to the South to study the problem and eventually solved the problem. He used prisoners in experiments, which was a common practice at that time. He had controlled groups, some eating only corn, and others eating corn and bread. He proved that pellagra was not contagious, a mistaken conclusion that authorities had drawn.

I think that science and technology should be thought of as separate. We should pay attention to technology, and give scientists the same freedom as artists. What they do is really harmless, but interesting, especially to other scientists.

*Nobel Prize in Chemistry, 1993

Philippe Busquin*
The European Parliament and research

I am here in this political space and I want to talk about the "body politic". The "body politic" is this Parliament and I would like to underline how important it is that Luca Coscioni Association has come here today, since I was in Rome in occasion of their first meeting. Here at the European Parliament you are at the heart of the debate between science and politics in terms of power and decisions. In the coming days we will have the opportunity to talk more about this, since the political debate is going to be more and more linked to the scientific one.

It is true that at the time of Copernicus and Galileo the issue was to understand whether the Earth revolved around the Sun or *vice versa*, and it is also true that this issue was particularly important for the Church, since certain truths started to be questioned. But today the problem is that the scientific development concerns life, its understanding and its modification. Therefore, we are facing an issue involving significant ethical questions for all of us, while, obviously, there is also the influence of dogmas and religions, that would like to control research itself.

We have experienced that and an emblematic example is the one of the embryonic stem cells. On that occasion, as you said – I was European Commissary for Research at that time – there were very hard and difficult debates at the European Parliament. Thinking about what Mr. Sabine has just said, I remember that we could obtain from the European Parliament the authorization to do some research thanks to the testimony of a deputy, who was in the position to affirm that he would let the research proceed, although, at the beginning, he had been philosophically against researching on embryos.

It is because of the definition of embryo that this issue is so problematic and this is because it involves a definition for life, for its starting moment and its end, as it happened also with the debate on euthanasia. And it is fundamental to recognize how extremely complicated it is to address those issues politically. The EU Parliament is the place where it is decided either to sustain research programs or, which is more important, to do research at the European level. And if at a certain point thousands researchers would focus on a promising field of the research, it would be for us a way to give a contribution to people's life. Well, if there is a chance to have faster results for citizens, for patients, it is then a political act to give space to and allow research.

Beyond these theoretic considerations I would like to point out some of the financing difficulties for the development of research. Both the research in itself and its financing are dependant from private and public entities. And in this context a political decision has to be taken: either to finance the most needed research or the most applied one. These are choices that are often at the center of the debates. And so I would like firstly to stress out again how in the debate on embryonic stem cells, there has been a pressure from Churches, particularly the Vatican but also some protestant Churches, aimed at biasing a democratic debate since it had not to be based on scientific knowledge but on dogmas. And more precisely, this pressure wanted to impose these dogmas to members of the parliament. It is quite a simple question: if electors are influenced to think that who touches an embryo is a criminal, a member of the Parliament, even if he has a shared point of view inside it, will think twice before supporting a research in that field. This is the political reality connected to research. Obviously, it involves also other fields, but stem cell research has been an European level issue.

What is possible to do at a State level and what at a European level? Because there is a different legitimacy. Marco just said that in Italy legislation is much stricter than in Britain. These are the two extreme positions. But this is how you can perceive the main question in this context: what is doable in Europe when you have different countries with different positions? A compromise solution is that it is possible to finance research in Europe but in the respect of every single country's legislation on research. Therefore, for example, stem cell research is allowed at European level and Minister Soria will come in the afternoon to tell us about what he did in Andalusia, as that region has a different legislation from the rest of Spain and it was then possible to perform some research otherwise illegal, while in Italy it is impossible to finance research on embryonic stem cells since it is forbidden by law.

What is complicated is to create a European space to perform research. It is clear that we face the same kind of constraint in a wider global perspective. For example, the Bush administration did not allow research in this field with public funds, in a rather hypocritical way as private societies were instead authorized to do it. Therefore there is a fundamental problem for scientific research because we, as Mr. Mullis said, work on pure science even if capable to have a quick application in technologies relevant for living beings. Clearly, this is challenging for the different philosophical and religious views. In a parallel manner, there are the ethic committees: in many countries hospitals themselves have an ethic committee defining strategies regarding abortion and life. But this is as to "outsource" freedom.

If we want to produce a legislation we have to face power struggles among different ideas and political influences. Therefore this is why I believe that it is truly fundamental to give place to a wide and public debate and to improve communication. Your testimony is a positive example of communication aimed at letting citizens understand problems and issues and making them realize that scientists are not wizards. Who spoke in favor of embryonic stem cells has been labeled as a Frankenstein to be demonized.

This does not mean that the limits of science interacting with human beings should not be questioned. For example there is the concept of human enhancement currently under discussion here at the EU parliament. It is about the desire to improve the human being. The most ordinary (and perhaps also superficial) way to look at this issue is doping in sports. Nowadays it is still not clear the difference between a medical therapy and an improvement of performances. For example with the development of new cognitive sciences, with neuroscience, it is clear how certain drugs can highly improve concentration. Where does the therapy end and where does the improvement, the modification of the human being start? There is a world-shared perspective to face this issue: UNESCO is concerned with it and has created a world Committee of Ethics, Sciences, Technologies and Bioethics. But there are also relevant influences clearly coming from religions, influences of some presumptive evidences and – as Marco (Cappato) correctly reminded - at the United Nations it was somehow set a point because of a tight vote on banning all kinds of therapeutic cloning, something extremely different from bare cloning.

I would like to add two or three elements. It is not enough to say that you want to do research but you need to stress out how you are going to finance it. Political choices are central in the decision-making process over scientific research. In order to deny space to an unwanted issue it is sufficient not to finance the research and that is a way to avoid research progress, so it is necessary to set up some priorities.

Not later than yesterday we were in this same hall for a meeting about research in developing countries. What kind of research is performed there? On what diseases do they make case studies? Do they study rare diseases or even more complicated unknown ones, if these affect a population that is not rich enough to access the necessary medical care? For example, all those issues are not properly considered in Africa, where there is not much space for research. It is possible to understand that there are differences of view on priorities, but still! There is a world trend to aid the development of this research without any commercial aim but with an humanitarian one, as it has already been witnessed. Therefore, it is important that material support allocated to research is aimed at the freedom of research, not to be deemed - as it is usually common nowadays - an "oriented" one, as they call it, but a research whose results cannot be foreseen. Scientists know that it was not through the orientation for researchers that it has been possible to achieve the most important scientific results, in fact it was usually the possibility to research freely that brought to the greatest results. You cannot decide in advance what you are exactly going to find. And in this perspective the EU program has a peculiarity. I remind the Fifth Framework Programme for Research: basically it was necessary a business plan in order to receive EU subsidies for research in my opinion that was not a good method as it obliged to know and communicate in advance the content of the research. It proved to be a method far from helping fundamental research, and therefore true research.

Therefore there are both material and institutional obstacles to research. I have just given you an example of the EU Parliament difficulties in finding a majority to define the financing of research in certain fields. Moreover, there are now more and more difficulties due to mechanisms, an example of which could be the one related to the mechanism of patents. From yesterday, March 17, we have here at the Parliament also a debate over intellectual property, as the seizing of parts of an intellectual property is what thwarts a researcher to proceed into a particular field. We have certain examples in the fields of genetics and breast cancer research, where a society that took patents did not allow the start of research on the base of certain documents. We had yesterday a debate here at the Parliament over free software, as the property of components as well as the creative rights over software can prevent the progress of research in the field of free computer technology.

Therefore you have seen how the matter is not just the single idea of research. At a certain point you can also produce extremely important declaration of principles, but then you have to analyze other practical sides of the issue: the financing, the bans, technical issues as the one of the patents, all problems troubling research development. So, there is a whole field of information that has to be free to make the research public. It is true that here we are not in the United States but also there we could not have a complete debate, as they cannot tackle the issue of patents and intellectual property rights there. It is an essential consideration because if somebody into a biotech lab finds a protein essential for life and wants to protect it, how can we stop him? Fortunately it is a bit more complicated than this. And it is this complexity that allows us to advance.

I would like to point out that nowadays there are also philosophical and political questions regarding evolution, Darwin and the relation between animals and human beings. Here at the EU Parliament we are debating on animal testing as we set – and this is democracy and freedom of thought - a direction towards extraordinary things, as, for example, setting structures to protect invertebrates. It is impossible to define where this issue starts and it ends, but the bare reality is that science is not a total abstraction. Such an emotional side plays an important role as a restraint to freedom of research. Because we do not consider acceptable to make experiments over primates and it is not hard, following the actual evolution of science, that it will be otherwise in the future, but nowadays it is impossible to transfer essential techniques and elements on human beings. About animal testing I would like to point out that it is an harsh topic to debate at the EU Parliament and during the next weeks we will tackle some proposals potentially dangerous for scientific research around the world as well as some other philosophical and historical issues. For example in Asia there is a problem concerning organ transplants since it is forbidden to touch dead bodies. Such a philosophy is respectable, but you need to consider what could be, in my opinion, a better humanism, capable of improving human beings, obviously avoiding dangerous excesses and the bad use of science. Because it is not science to be good or bad but it is the use you make of it.

I would like to end pointing out that the bigger risk for research, in Europe at least, is the lack of researchers, since in our societies nowadays the attractiveness of science is unfortunately diminishing. When we check out statistics of European countries we discover less and less researchers of pure science or life science, mainly potential PhDs and researchers. This is an essential point. Why this lack of researchers? Of course there is a variety of causes: in every case we know that if in Europe we want to respect the aim of the 3% GDP devolved to research, there should be around 500,000 – 800,000 researchers every year. We cannot and we should not pay foreign brains as it is neither ethical nor correct, but specially, not efficient as there is a worldwide permeation: all the issues are interconnected and for example climate research is as important in Africa than it is in Europe. And therefore this thwarts brain escapes. But on the other side in Europe, there is a lack of fascination for science for a burning reason: in my opinion, the scientific research - which is a promethean path – is being reconsidered because of a certain use that has been made of scientific development, e.g. climate change, human footprint over nature and the ecosystem.

All these issues characterize a slightly blurred situation, what in mathematics we call "blurred logic", where it is not clear where we are going and this can be very emotional and difficult. It is about the use that is made of fears – because this is what lies at the core of the issue - in the context of the return to the "heady" values of religion and of the simplification of knowledge. It is about values still full of meaning here and therefore I believe that we have to be very careful about it, if we want to look after freedom of research. That is in the Fundamental Rights Chart.

I have loved that image that you should not frame a picture. It should not be possible to frame research into a dogmatic context.

*MEP; former Commissioner for Science and Research

Past and future
of scientific freedom

Emma Bonino*
The right to knowledge

Mr. Minister (Bernat Soria), I feel compelled to say how pleased I am to be a member of this panel along with your good self. One of the first occasions when I heard you speak was in Geneva at the Commission of Human Rights, at an initiative organised by the Radical Party in not entirely fruitless opposition to the initiative launched by the Vatican and the United States to prohibit stem cell research. Instead of approaching the Scientific Commission, we correctly approached the Commission on Human Rights. I believe that it is thanks to your motion relating to the right to knowledge, knowledge of value, that the right has remained substantially in place. We then met again in Campidoglio, at the First Congress, again in the company of scientists, and now I find you here. I do not know which of the two professions you are most drawn to, but I am happy that you are the minister. In Italy, we have another well-known scientist, Professor Veronesi, who was also a minister for a short time in the past; I think he did not have an easy life neither. In actual fact I found in your contribution and, indeed, in everything I have heard this morning, countless reasons to consolidate what we have achieved so far. The aim of this Congress is to set up a permanent structure in the defence of freedom for scientific research in all fields in which it is threatened.

In my opinion, this morning's session has been very important. I believe that this bringing together victims of disease, politicians, the curious and scientists is a very useful change of direction. Many speeches have caused me to reflect on matters which had never previously occurred to me. I was very interested, for example, in the distinction made by Professor Mullis between science and applied technology - this is actually a distinction I had never considered before, but it is really very illuminating. Once understood, it becomes automatic that if the government is interested, it is interested in applied technology and not science. Obviously, I should have liked to be a good deal more, shall we say, long-winded about this, as a politician; however, I must remember that I am Italian and hence subjected to all these matters in a situation of the greatest difficulty. I am experiencing this meeting with yourselves almost as a Mayday call, a cry for help for the truth. The situation in which we find ourselves at the moment is characterised by the adoption by the entirety of public opinion, based to some extent on the messages it receives, of an unscientific, if not actually anti-scientific, attitude; an attitude which means that anyone described as a researcher, or all the more a scientist, receives no positive acceptance as a researcher at all, and is viewed more as a warlock devoted to causing harm, or to manipulating or even attacking everything which is seen as "positive" where I come from, and which, heaven knows why, is thought of as "natural". The word "natural", of course, is seen as meaning "good", healthy; as we know, this is not actually the case. As I see it, it is the struggle of humanity with nature which has been one of the powerful engines of our humanity.

In Italy, not only research suffer under the kind of conditions which have already been outlined, and which others can describe in greater detail, but is to be found in a situation which, when compared with the data presented today, might genuinely explain the reason why, when others hear the story, we may well find ourselves being asked exactly what is going on in our country. In Italy, it is even quite difficult to lay your hands on the morning-after pill, which has given rise, among other things, to a whole philosophical – and certainly unscientific – debate. On the matter of abortion, for example, in Italy we have been battling for over ten years - in fact nearly twenty - to be permitted to use RU486, and still without success. We are still bombarded by so-called scientific publications claiming to demonstrate the harmfulness of RU486 by stating how many women have died because of it. In actual fact, when the matter is examined a little more clearly, it turns out that RU486 had nothing to do with it. I could quote thousands of similar examples. Recently we have been involved in a "debate" on the Englaro case, concerning living will, in which yet again religious and ideological information, highly respectable or not (this is not the point), dominated the argument, and where, yet again, individual freedom, the freedom of the citizen, is seen as a powerful threat and to be greatly feared. That means that everybody here, whether holding an Italian passport, or with an interest in Italy, sees this Congress as a cry for help. And we shall cling to this Congress, and all the proposals made here, including that of the institutionalisation of this Congress, as a bulwark from which we can derive strength.

I can assure you that defending freedom of research, and freedom of choice in general, is no easy matter. This morning our Romanian

Christian Democrat member of Parliament, Daniel Petru Funeriu, in his brief address, most clearly outlined the problem of the absolute necessity of separating the religious sphere of activities from the public or secular sphere. The problem is that among us this is not so easy, since the idea is very widespread that the Church is the only body possessing values, such as life and the defence of life, and that all other organisations defend no values at all. But what we have been listening to, not to mention our own experiences and the dramas in our own lives, tell us very clearly that this is not the case. On the contrary, they reveal to us the relationship between theory and humanity, between theory and the flesh and blood of hundreds of thousands of human beings, whose hopes lie in present and future scientific discoveries.

Yesterday I took part in a meeting on "Women and Science" in Paris, attended mainly by women from the Arab world. I was particularly impressed by the contribution from François D'Aubert, former Minister for Research and currently president of the Cité des Sciences et de l'Industrie, who together with the Director of the Institut Pasteur, Professor Alice Dautry, and based on scientific results achieved over the past few years, gave us a brief history of progress as it has affected health. It is really surprising how, as soon as research and the results obtained from it are in use, such as in medication which is suddenly widespread and common, they are taken for granted, as though everybody had forgotten that they are the fruit of years and years of research, of freedom to research, of investment, support and everything we have talked about this morning.

This congress has been planned as the second meeting in the wake of the Rome session. I find it hard to believe that the situation with regard to dogma and ideology which we are experiencing here in Italy is unique to Italy. It is my belief, and my fear, that if we do not resist this highly reactionary and freedom-denying *modus operandi* with enormous energy, it may become contagious and drag not only the Italian political classes backwards, but all the others, too. Sometimes I experience the ecclesiastical hierarchy's interfering in personal decisions as an attempt to carry the final trench, from which they can return and spread throughout the whole world.

In this light it is with the greatest of anxiety that we await the decisions which President Obama must soon make, hoping that they may augur the turning of a new page, following the somewhat retrograde and even destructive outcomes of the alliance of the Bush administration with other countries and institutions. These three days are an opportunity for us to understand what needs to be done, and I am sure that a whole raft of proposals are in the process of preparation.

I shall be very interested to hear what Nobel Laureate Perl has to say on the conversion of military structures or military research into civil research, a subject which we have tackled in past years and which I feel is as important a topic as ever. Professor Veronesi, whom I have already mentioned, is also trying out, among other things, an experiment of this type in Italy, based on the conversion of military spending.

So it is my conviction that pooling all our forces, be they legal, scientific, political, be they concerned with communication or indeed all the professions, might perhaps be the best way to find this strength. This Second World Congress is not a world congress for scientists, but a world congress for freedom of scientific research, and the reason is because, in my opinion, we do not only need the commitment of the scientists but also the synergies which arise from other aspects of the social and political life of a country. It is certainly a very ambitious project, but it is one which grows more essential with the passing of time. I had not, for example, thought of your proposal that we accept the situation as a reflection of the current crisis. I have thought about the way the crisis is a shock to Europe, to the internal market and the euro, but I had not given any thought to a theoretical way out, certainly one which would be different, nontraditional. I should like to highlight the three or four innovative directions arising from this initiative: synergy, the bringing together of different sections of society, determination and the idea of making it a permanent structure. I can say that, as Radicals, this is a project on which we intend to work very hard and for which I feel we are now better prepared, having already worked hard in the past few years on many other projects, such as, for example, at a time when it was hard to believe it, in 2000-2001, we tried to draw attention to new dimensions, such as the human genome.

It is, in fact, a problem, as we came to realise, that the political classes find themselves having to tackle some problems in a state of complete unreadiness, having never given any prior thought to the possible implications. My hope is that this commitment as a political force may be successful in attracting others, since I see it not as a left/right question, but a question of freedom, and I think that from this point of view we also have something different and fresh to say. Thank you for your commitment.

*Vice-President, Italian Senate;
former European Commissioner

Bernat Soria*
**The experience of Spain
for freedom of scientific research and cure**

Many thanks for this opportunity to be here with you. I am willing to tell you what a researcher, who dedicated his life to the research in a laboratory and his last years to stem cells and diabetes, thinks when he becomes Minister of Health in a democratic government.

A Friday I was called by the Prime Minister whom I knew for sure although I had always been working in a laboratory and never involved in politics, nonetheless he proposed to me to become a minister of his cabinet and I accepted. The next Monday I set in the cabinet myself. I had not thought of what it means to be a minister, but during the last year and a half, since I became active in the field of politics as a minister, I have been keeping my research group, too, and I have been thinking about the power of politics and the opportunity to solve problems I could not solve as a mere researcher.

First of all I want to speak of the value of scientific research and of its impact on society and on social values. Science is a value we have got and one that has an impact on other social values. Science represents a value because of this impact on society, law and technology, but much more when the scientific method and knowledge are accepted as a tool to build society. This is true if seen from an economic, ethical, political point of view and much more. In the contxt of a democratic society, scientific ethics represents a service for the humanity. In the context of a democratic society some decisions have an economic impact but research in certain fields, that I am going to comment, goes beyond the economic relevance; a healthcare system using these results makes innovation available for patients. Moreover costs are cut down and cures are more viable.

How was Spain until 2004 and how did it change from 2004 to 2008, that is during the first legislature of Socialist government, where I took part in during its last time? In 2004 scientific research suffered a set of restrictions, be they legal - since we needed a framework to develop our research -, religious, ethical or cultural, but also financial restrictions. In fact the pharmaceutical industry is not always interested in a certain pathway of research and I would like to comment not only the case of stem cells but of rare diseases and orphan drugs, since they are addressed to a limited group of patients, that is a niche market, not to be funded by the pharmaceutical industry. This is a situation we have tried to solve. Before 2007 scientific research was limited by a set of rules, but in some aspects we could make research. We needed a new law which was issued during our last legislature, that is a law concerning biomedical research, together with another law on assisted reproduction, which authorized and ruled the use of embryonic material. Moreover it analysed the ethical, political and economic aspects concerning genetic tests. It authorized the nuclear transfer, it ruled the procedure and I would like to comment it. In fact, you talk about ethics – and for the last 10 years hundreds of people have been talking about it with me and any researcher working on embryonic stem cells – and other aspects of medical ethics, such as the genetic diagnosis or the knowledge of human genome, which are relevant in the field of biomedical research, although they are not considered with due attention. This law helped Spain adopting a legal framework comparable to the United Kingdom, Sweden, Singapore and other countries where research is not only authorized but also duly ruled. In fact research does not only need to be authorized but also ruled so that juridical consequences are clear for researchers and whoever works on it. How did the situation change? Let's show some figures: until 2004 there had been no project of research on embryonic stem cells, but only two projects concerning rare diseases and orphan drugs and in 2008 we had got 65 projects concerning embryonic stem cells in Spain along with 36 on orphan drugs and rare diseases. The government is financing 65 projects through 120 millions. A Health Minister has got means to finance projects and establish priorities since a politician is responsible for telling you what you should investigate and what we want to solve: this is the mandate we have been given by citizens. The sum of money we dedicated in Spain raised from 2,900 million euro to around 8,000 million euro in a short legislature. The political responsibility does not only consist in deciding what we can investigate, but also how we fund that research. As a researcher, when I was asked what I did need to make research, I replied: both a change in the regulation and a financial budget. Changing the law is not enough. You need to fund projects, too, otherwise you never get results.

I will comment very rapidly since many fields are affected by these limitations, not only research with stem cells, but also orphan drugs and other fields. In all these cases we have legal, cultural, religious or economical limitations, which hamper the development of research in a lot of fields. As a Minister, among my first provisions, I created a general direction for advanced therapies, to facilitate new therapies for those pathologies for which there is no solution yet. The government should push for new therapies where there is none. Launching calls is not enough; you must say: "Let's go this way", because citizens require that and I sit in that cabinet because citizens put me there. What I did was to create a general direction for advanced therapies and transplants. As you may know, Spain is number one in the world as for organ transplants; we have expertise in transplants of tissues and cells. But we are also willing to be pioneers, so we approved a law, which is still in force - the law on assisted reproduction and biomedical research.

When you want to develop an area, you also need training along with regulation. When we started to research stem cells, we noticed that a few researchers knew them. There were good cell biologists, good molecular biologists, good developmental biologists and so on but they were to be trained. Moreover, we must train technicians to work according to GMP (Good Manufacturing Practice), since we want that clinical trials follow to that research. To that purpose we do not only need regulations: we need to train people; to launch our Spanish Medicines Agency to be part of the European Agency; to open a section to evaluate, register and authorize new therapies; to open an unit for the so-called independent research, that is generally the kind of research not funded by the pharmaceutical industry. We are promoting the creation of a European forum for advanced therapies, we need to build clean rooms according to GMP and to develop infrastructures along with funds and these resources.

In conclusion I would like to reflect on a further point, that is the value of freedom of research during the economic crisis. The financial crisis worldwide touches every activity, including the political and cultural one. The governments meet, the Euro-group meets, they undertake actions, help the bank sector, small enterprises, there are severe financial problems. Freedom of research can help us finding a solution. This is the reflection of a researcher who now is a minister, hence it is not an economist's reflection, nor the thought of an expert in crisis, but I would like to share my opinion with you. In the last 200 years we went through around five technological revolutions: the industrial revolution; the steel revolution; the railway revolution; the revolution of advanced engineering; the last revolution concerned oil and the mass production, the production of cars. Each revolution encountered a crisis in the middle. Therefore we cannot exclude that we are going through the crisis of the today's technological revoution. Today's technological revolution is the information revolution. Look at the curve representing the evolution of technological revolution: first of all there is a phase of bing bang, the explosion of anything, the knowledge of anything having a big impact; afterwards you have a franticness, a very rapid rhythm supported by huge investments. This franticness bursts into the crisis, then we solve it and enter a synergy that is a golden phase consisting in an increased social wealth and even richness. So this technological revolution comes to its end, it reaches its top and its stability at last. Each crisis goes through this curve: for instance the franticness of the Twenties, that is a moment of happiness, when everybody bought, was happy, the art and the culture developed, there was an extraordinary moment of explosion. Then the crisis of '29 came and the Thirties wanted a strong regulation. A phase of stability followed to that. After the Second World War we entered a further stage of wealth. Then the sensation is that we are going through the crisis of the information revolution, due to the new information and communication technologies. It also consisted in a starting phase, a phase of franticness between 1990 and 2000, i.e. the crisis of the "dot com". We are in the middle of it. In my opinion every technological revolution passes a phase of crisis in the middle, until it meets its place in the society. I believe that freedom of scientific research is very important to go out from this crisis, since it entails freedom to research options. Nobody knows how we will get out of this crisis, but if we are not free to raise different solutions it will be difficult to find out the best one. Nobody knows the rule, moreover nobody predicted it rightly: neither the best economist nor the sociologists predicted what is passing now. In my opinion, knowledge, innovation and, for granted, freedom may help us getting well out of this crisis.

Secondly, knowledge may create wealth when there are social structures which allow the transfer of that knowledge. Take for instance the Spanish national healthcare system. Spain is a young democracy, it is only 30 years old; in the last 20 years this young democracy generated a national healthcare system which is universal, public and for free. The first Socialist government created that in 1986 and now the Spanish national healthcare system is deemed to be one of the world's best. In 2008 the international reports referred that we are the 4th best while in 2001 we were the 6th; a good national healthcare system however. How can you measure whether we are the best in the field of organ donations and transplants? I mean whether our health indicators are good or not? Let's take for instance a due reference: United States. United States are the first economic power in the world. They are the first in research as well, but they are not the first as far as it concerns health. This is a very important rule, because we researchers, we all state that our projects are aimed at raising knowledge which will be good for health and will generate social well-being. All the good and great researchers we have in Italy and in Europe, like Elena Cattaneo and Giulio Cossu, write that in the first sentence of their projects proposals. We have an example here of the way the first power in the world, the first economic power in the world breaks over this statement. For this reason President Obama's programme is focused on the reform of the healthcare system. They lack a transfer system from knowledge to patients. There is a system to transfer the knowledge to the pharmaceutical industry and produce well-being, but in the United States they have not got a system to transfer it to patients.

On the contrary we efficiently manage our healthcare system in Spain and this is my responsibility as a minister now: we spend 1,300 euro a year per inhabitant, while in the United States they spend three times as much. In the field of healthcare you may use several indicators: life expectancy at birth, child mortality and so on. As for child mortality, Spain is the 3rd best in the world, while United States are the 19th. Therefore the first conclusion is that we need a system to transfer the knowledge to the patients and a good national healthcare system, to be universal, i.e. including all patients, if we want research to generate social freedom. That is, we do not only need to research in certain areas; we do not only need to fund and manage that structure. Spain has got a lower average rent, nonetheless we have four years more life expectancy than United States, thanks to our structure to share "healthcare".

We want that society generates its values from a form of scientific thinking and no other forms of thinking; they are all legitimate but I defend that the scientific knowledge does not only generate knowledge, but values in the society. Secondly, we must change the legislation, including not only stem cells but other fields which are subject to restrictions and which are important for patients, e.g. orphan drugs, rare diseases, non-commercial research. Take for instance what happens to authorized drugs which are already marketed but have adverse effects: who will monitor them? Who is interested in researching cheaper drugs? The government is, since the market does not profit of a cheaper drug even though it is a good one. I dedicated almost my entire life to diabetes and there you have good drugs with one defect: they are very cheap, hence industry does not research such. So the government must do that.

Lastly, I must say that I am convinced that knowledge, innovation and freedom of research may help us getting out of this crisis and that in order to benefit from knowledge we need structures which transfer the knowledge to all – I repeat all – citizens, be they poor or rich, be they from the North or the South, both the ones suffering from a very common disease or a rare one.

Question by Danny Reviers, *chairman of ALS LIGA, Belgium:*
I am an ALS patient. Amyotrophic lateral sclerosis is a degenerative disease - a "motor neurone disease" is what is called in English. People's status degenerates very quickly. Sometimes they only have five, even three years after their diagnoses. It degenerates so that we cannot breathe, we can no longer speak. In addition to this there is no treatment for that disease, so of course people end up in a very desperate situation and they become so desperate that they end up seeking any therapy abroad. Sometimes, they get in touch with researchers in countries which have not the best intentions, perhaps in countries where there is less regulation in rendering stem cell therapies, for example. People regularly travel to China where they end up spending 30,000 euro for a couple of hours treatment, then of course that therapy does not work. The only aim of those scientists is to get money out of those people. This is a very serious situation, we have been combating all heartedly. Therapies are now emerging all around Europe: in Germany, the Netherlands, Belgium. Treatments were banned in the past, nevertheless people are so wealthy that they end up purchasing treatments with stem cells. There are people treated and getting their embryos implanted a couple of weeks later somewhere else. Those people cannot be held liable. Stem cell research already exists to a large extent. We need to make more efforts. My own vision in this respect is that we need to support each other. When we talk about cycling, football, championships, we are like enemies. But as for stem cell therapy and human lives, we have to move in the same direction. I am delighted to see there is so much progress in Spain. Would you like to take on a pioneering role in promoting it in Europe?

Minister Soria: I am. I know this pathology very well: amyotrophic lateral sclerosis is a neurodegenerative disease which it progressively leads to the paralysis and to death. It is an example of neurodegenerative diseases for which there is no kind of treatment. Stem cells are one of the probabilities that we are researching. But I am informed that to date nobody can grant a treatment hence we cannot recommend it. We must persuade patients that some charlatans with little ethics advertise on the internet by charging abusive prices so that families have to sell their properties in order to get a treatment with no effect. The desperation of the family of the patients is easy to understand but no serious scientist, no physician can recommend those treatments.

What we do need is to authorise, to finance and to regulate. Regulating is needed, since any new therapeutic proposal must be analysed by an ethical committee in charge of clinical trials, that is an efficient system to test whether there are scientific basis for the proposals, by considering both the risk the new treatment may entail and the value of the scientific plan so that we can conclude whether this proposal is positive, neutral or negative for patients' health. First of all we authorised that kind of research in Spain; secondly, we funded it. I remember at least a group researching stem cells and amyotrophic lateral sclerosis, but maybe there are more. Finally, we regulated. It means that a new treatment or a new drug in Spain are authorised by the Spanish Medicines Agency which is part of the EMEA. When the process works, we can help all Europe getting this treatment, through an European authorization and more probably a certification to facilitate the proceeding. What I have already done in Spain is to limit the proceeding to two tracks for the authorization: the normal track, which is very slow, for new molecules, except for innovating molecules for some types of cancer which degenerate very quickly; the other track of authorization and evaluation is targeted to advanced therapies, including amyotrophic lateral sclerosis. This track also requires patients' safety and quality of the process but it is much more rapid since we know that we do not have much time.

Once I was struck by a sentence - I was speaking with some patients and one of them, affected by ALS like you, asked me: "When will stem cells help treating this disease?" and I replied what I am replying to you: first of all, nobody can grant that there will be a treatment, not even in the future. We could only reply that we were not allowed to research. First of all you need to research so that you can see whether you can find out a solution like that. But the patient went on and asked: "How long does it take to know whether this is the right pathway or not?". A scientist can hardly say, so I replied: "Give me five years time", provided that scientific projects usually last five years - I did not mean that I was going to be able to answer. And the patient replied: "I do not have five years time". To this purpose I have created a rapid authorization track for that kind of trials in Spain. This is the only way since we cannot go more rapidly. The only way is doing well, that is not purchasing miraculous treatments, since they do not exist. "Going on time there, where we can go", I have not got a better answer. I would like, but I do not believe that I can give a better one.

One of the things I have experienced being minister of the government is that I have lost freedom. As a scientist, I could make comments about everything, but as a minister, I cannot comment other countries' politics. I cannot make comments on Italy - it is a friend of Spain, we collaborate in many ways. I have made a sure reference to USA, because in the past I gave lectures in Washington. We are collaborating with the new administration in this sense. So, I cannot break my commitment. I should not make comments about other countries' politics.

Secondly, I consider it very difficult to reach a conclusion, which is practical or regulatory for all the countries. If you consider abortion by example, in Europe there are different laws. There are two countries in which there are strong limitations or it is forbidden. So, those aspects in which ethics are involved are extremely difficult if not impossible to regulate at an international level. That is something that each country will solve. So, I could make comments about what the UK has done, their decision to destroy the supernumerary embryos. We know there are many remaining embryos, but we do not need all of them, because these embryos were not created for this aim. But it is important – and I will end with this comment - to ask the couples: what do you want to do with your embryos? We did the survey before and later. We did the survey before we knew that the stem cells could have a therapeutic use - in that case 40-50% of the people said yes. But when the people knew that embryos could have a therapeutic use, more than 90% in Spain said yes. We will authorize the embryos to be used in research. We are producing new cell lines, too - we have about 20 new cell lines. We are now producing cell lines with particular mutations, what is relevant to study a disease, in order to know how it appears. We did some progress, but all these lines have been produced through new supernumerary embryos thanks to the couples' consent. What will happen to the rest of embryos? I really do not know. At least, thanks to the new law we issued in 2006 - a new law for human assisted reproduction – Spain is very active. We gave several options for the embryos. Supernumerary embryos could be used for research, could be kept, could be destroyed. It depends on the couples. They decide.

*Minister of Health, Spain

64

Elena Cattaneo*
The Italian case and the Spanish example

Following this morning's interesting and stimulating debate it is both a pleasure and an honour to be leading this session, having confirmed, understood and learnt of the many obstacles we must yet overcome.

Knowing Europe's great strength gives us the kind of hope thanks to which we may one day become able to use our lives and skills towards the common good, and where the latter includes understanding of, and hope for, the kind of illnesses we mentioned this morning.

When I started my job at the University of Milan, as a researcher, I fell in love with my work – I have been a researcher for twenty years now; however I had not yet understood how much it was synonymous with freedom and, I must say, now that I have understood this, it is even clearer why I cannot do without it. Truly, the value of research goes well beyond the yielded data - it is its ability to suggest ideas that will then undergo the rigorous scrutiny of science from the laboratory bench; it is the possibility it gives for self-criticism, for debate. In my opinion, this is the meaning of freedom, and one without which we neither can nor ought to be.

It is precisely for this reason that the first speaker of the session is particularly interesting: he is the researcher Bernat Soria, who is also the Spanish Minister of Health. I must admit that as an Italian researcher residing on the Southern side of the Alps I look upon the Spanish scenario with enthusiasm, for it distinguishes itself by a thriving research, an attentive government, and a set of procedures which are consistently implemented. Among the many positive aspects that impress me is how my research peers in Spain respond with pride when asked about the health of their country's science administration, agencies, ANEP (the agency evaluating the majority of research projects in Spain) and methods of releasing public funding - a serious problem in Italy. I always ask myself why we cannot become equally proud: I believe that in Italy, as in other backward-looking States and in the whole of Europe, we must aim to turn science into not only common heritage but also an instrument through which we may become better citizens of a wider nation.

I wish to thank the Spanish Minister of Health for his precise speech, laden with data and positive experiences. I also wish to stress how Bernat Soria has been one of the founders of embryo stem cell research for diabetes, and that his team was the first to both attempt and succeed in this area. Perhaps we must be grateful that he was not punished for this, as may have happened had he lived in other countries.

I would like to go back to one of the many remarks he has shared with us, namely the initial one concerning the importance of continuously changing and reviewing legislation. While I wholeheartedly agree on this point I wish to add that this is insufficient: we also need funding. What we saw yesterday in Italy proves that legislation *per se* is insufficient: there we have legislative restrictions on research with embryonic stem cells, except where said cells have already been obtained; this allows my and other laboratories to put forward research proposals and to carry out research also on research with embryonic stem cells. However, this amounts to false hope after the government announcing that future funds for stem cell research applications will exclude research with embryonic stem cells. As John Harris has reminded us in his morning speech, this hypocrisy is all too clear when we consider that the Italian government will never renounce the benefits derived from such research, now and in the future, just like the Bush administration, which halted public funding for such research but never outlawed it.

Fortunately for us and our citizens, allowing embryo stem cell research has yielded results of the utmost importance, such as the reprogrammed cells discovered by a Japanese and an American team: the latter was able to continue its research not only because there was no ban in the US but also because it received continued financial support by foundations and private citizens. In contrast to this, Italian researchers will now find themselves unable to receive any funding, what will put them in the situation where they will be able to receive European funding for such research but excluded from it in their own State: does this not constitute a smokescreen?

*Director, Centre for Stem Cell Research, University of Milan, Italy;
Coordinator of NeuroStemCell Consortium

Gilberto Corbellini*
Retrospectives and prospects on the freedom of science from the viewpoint of a historian

The second edition of the World Congress for Freedom of Scientific Research should represent the opportunity to both highlight and discuss more systematically the reasons that hinder the recognition of the role that science and its practical effects, including the social diffusion of a scientific culture, have been playing for the promotion of human social and economic well-being. Moreover, it would be useful to discuss the most effective strategies which could keep down the effects of the political actions aimed to either restraining the freedom of scientific research or even manipulating science, be they inspired by religious or non religious anti-democratic ideologies, or springing from formally anti-totalitarian positions which nonetheless dangerously misunderstand the relationship between science and democracies.

However, the debate about the freedom of science cannot leave the context aside, better said the plurality of political and economic settings within which science is produced. And as we all know, the problems scientists face vary a lot depending on these contexts. Probably, one aspect that could be considered as being quite transversal is represented by the apparent paradox indicating that wherever people's wellbeing has greatly increased thank to scientific and technological progresses, distrusts and cultural oppositions towards science and scientists are also very common. If you read carefully the periodic surveys on public perception of science, such as the Eurobarometer surveys, or the National Science Foundation, we get the important information that there seem to be greater reservations towards science and its consequences just in those countries where social wellbeing is more widely spread and where good quality science is produced. The citizens of those countries tend to focus more on the limits of science rather than on its potentials and they believe that scientific progress dangerously alter those natural balances which are necessary for a true human and environmental welfare.

In economically and socially less advanced countries - I am not addressing today those domestic situations where science is looked

on because of religious fundamentalism and total lack of civil freedom - expectations towards science are indeed more optimistic. Obviously in this context the impact of scientific progress on people's
well-being is more tangible namely as it provides the opportunity to
go beyond the typical constraints of a nature-dependent life. However, the development of an internal political and cultural environment to promote investment in scientific education, basic research
and innovation is a difficult goal to attain for these countries. Therefore, their development still relies heavily on import of technology
from advanced countries.

Perception toward science and technologies in the Western countries is heavily inclined to positively address scientific achievements
when they produce advantages, especially in terms of health improvement perspectives. On the other hand, criticism arises when
scientific progress does not have immediate functional implications
or when it happens to contrast with embedded ideas of the local cultural anthropology or with what is intuitively conceived as safer, if
not sacred. This tendency is epitomized by the predominant attitude,
especially in Western Europe, towards genetically modified organisms in the agriculture and food farming industry. Religious bias also
intervenes in the debate over reproduction and birth control alleging
these practices to pursue unnatural and then immoral expectations.
The implicit or common-sense idea of nature is becoming increasingly important in the cultural and political definition of ethically
controversial issues arisen by the discourse over the possibility for
scientific progress and its technological applications to improve
human condition, and on the related potential risks inevitably intertwined with any technological innovation. As you can notice by
the debate around the political use that has been made of the pre-
cautionary principle, it is quite paradoxical that scientific methods
are taken into account when assessing how 'natural' those processes
actually are, and what are the actual risks of the assumed interference of new technologies with such processes.

The geographic and especially the geopolitical context plays a
major role with regard to this situation. For instance, in Italy the not
only cultural but mainly political leverage of the Catholic Church is
to be considered to properly understand why and how scientists
have became synonymous of people who are threatening human
freedom and dignity.

A relevant and somehow recent aspect of these attacks against science and scientists is the manipulation of science by some other scientists that often cynically lend themselves to circulate misleading
information or endorse interpretations instrumental to some reli-

gious or ideological bias. The role of media is also crucial to this trend. In their effort to dramatize even the scientific debate, journalists usually present scientists as having contrasting visions on a given controversial issue, or they compare empirically established theories with theories that try to prove themselves by diverting the debate on an ideological level. Normally, in the media the tentative and provisional, but evidence-based character of scientific explanations are misrepresented as epistemological limits, while the illogical and populist demands for definitive answers or certainties are instrumentally emphasized.

These phenomena are also likely to be a consequence of the poor impact of all the rational arguments presented in the last decades to refute prejudices against science. It is also to be thoroughly considered that the neuropsychological features we possess because of our evolutionary origins may have a role in the general attitude to refuse or regard science as threatening human dignity and political democracy. After all, in recent years cognitive psychologists and evolutionists along with neurobiologists have indeed been competing to highlight the limits of our much praised rationality. One could speculate that the invention of the modern naturalistic or scientific thought provided in some contexts the conditions to develop rational behaviours leading to the emergence of democratic forms of social organizations. It is also well known that an adequate education fosters the level of individual autonomy needed to fully appreciate the advantages of freedom and self-determination.

Consequently, underperforming educational systems, especially in the scientific training, which are typical of countries where education is lead or influenced by religious institutions, do represent a relevant risk factor and may combine to maintain or to bring about totalitarian regimes and anti-scientific movements.

What are the effective strategies to be pursued in order to better analyse problems when facing such complex situations? Probably in the first place it is fundamental to adopt a self-distanced perspective to understand the origin of problems and to investigate those factors that are not immediately responsible for this situation, but that deeply affect the possibility to effectively address a problem. Owing to human psychologocal dynamics and to our brain processing, we do not relate objectively to historical experience, but we rather seek there to sort out elements that support preconceived ideas. Nonetheless any problem, including resistance to scientific progress in some geopolitical contexts, has a genealogy and evolves. For instance, the way religion and politics confront themselves with science has become more complex, and recalling the Galileo's trial or the Lyssenko's case could not always be the best approach to understand the current trends.

Nonetheless as seen in the history of science, science and scientific culture have faced many hurdles throughout modern and contemporary age. Such history shows repeating trends, like the anti-authoritarian and anti-traditionalist nature of science as a triggering factor of conflicts. Political, religious and cultural opposition thwarted scientific progress when it challenged cultural beliefs or grand visions favouring the acquisition of socially normative values, or when it had an impact on embedded cultural customs. Since cultural developments do not integrate in the genetic heritage of species, with every passing generation some achievements may also get lost, especially in terms of scientists' capability to communicate the importance of freedom of scientific research to society and to political actors.

Not only difficulties challenging science have historically evolved but also strategies adopted by the scientific community to rise above these problems. Sixty years ago, in the aftermath of the Universal Declaration of Human Rights and within the activities promoted by UNESCO to communicate the principles and values established in the 1948 Declaration, scientists began debating the issue of scientific freedom. The debate was affected by existing threats to scientific freedom, due to the emergence of totalitarian regimes between the two World Wars. The perception of the role of scientists during the II World War and the forecoming changes in the organization of scientific research in terms of an increased role of State and politics also played a role in the debate. Independently from the historical context, among others the debate came to the conclusion which is summarized in a 1950 book by astronomer Bart Bok, *Freedom in Science*: «Freedom of science cannot be maintained unless in the presence of a positive climate in world opinion». Bok's ideas were that scientists must commit themselves to communicate to society, that freedom of research is fundamental to achieve scientific and technological progress. Therefore, during the past century the scientific communities succeed in communicating to society that science relies on the best possible tools so far invented for solving problems. The results of the past century's strategies for promoting science were good but always fragile and uncertain, as it can be seen from the problems that science and scientists regularly face whenever new frontiers to knowledge open up, leading to consequences able to improve human well-being but also threaten, at the same time, the most popular and intuitive beliefs.

In the 60s and at the beginning of the 70s there was a greater number of scientists interested in the impact that the new biomedical sciences could produce on society. Prestigious researchers like Jacques Monod, Joshua Lederberg, Francis Crick, Salvador Luria, Konrad Lorenz, Jonas Salk, and many others, tried to build a bridge towards human sciences, claiming at the same time a cultural humanistic statute for science against the drift of a world of knowledge divided into "two cultures". Among the most important ideas of that time, that the scientific community sadly abandoned, we can see the demand for recognizing an ethical statute of scientific knowledge. This claim was based on a tradition of sociological studies, which was theoretically much more solid and plausible compared to the most recent approaches inspired by the epistemological relativism of postmodern sociologists. In the light of the evolution of the relationships between science and society for instance Jacques Monod's message keeps a non-instrumental relevance to present as it recognized an ethical choice in the scientists' support to the postulate of objectivity.

Bioethics and postmodern relativist epistemologies have played a very recent role in trying to confine science and culture in a new totally marginal position within the latest debate about the regulation and the educational strategies which can guarantee and improve the contribute of science and scientists to the citizens' civic awareness and society's civil progress. Inspired by traditional ethical disciplines and above all by a medical ethics based on abstractly defined absolute values, bioethics has probably run out of its propellant push. In their turn, the science and technology studies, that is the sociological approaches inspired by relativist epistemologies, naturally evolved towards an explicit politicization that is getting very close to sectarianism and integralism.

The UNESCO people are no more defending scientific freedom. Obviously influenced by the new climate, UNESCO has issued two important documents about bioethics in the last decade, i.e. the Universal Declaration on the Human Genome and the Universal Declaration on Bioethics and Human Rights. These documents strengthen a negative political and cultural perception of science since in some parts they exaggerate the risks related to genetic, genomic and cell biotechnology research developments which are in fact very minimal compared to the benefits that could be generated with regard to human life quality.

Do we also have some elements to be optimistic? I think, that conceptual and methodological progresses of neurobiological, psychological and evolutionistic research offer considerable opportunities for science to gain a more functional and constructive relationship with human sciences. For instance, this is remarkable within the field of neuroethics observations, where the most original and important developments do not originate from the so-called reflections on the ethics of neuroscience, but from the neuroscientific studies of ethics, aimed at empirically investigate the origin and the physiology of human morality, also from the social psychology and evolutionistic point of view.

How could it be possible to stimulate a general debate about the freedom of scientific research by taking into account the differences among the contexts and the new opportunities offered by the improvement of the scientific understanding of human sociality? Those who whish to pursue a scientific career and the institutions promoting science and its cultural implications should aim at providing socially useful values to be immediately acquired and perceived as means to the diffusion of individual freedom, trust and respect among people. The objective of scientific diffusion should be to provide citizens, especially children and adolescents who prepare themselves to fully take advantage of civil rights with the cultural instruments to understand the terms of controversies and acquire the knowledge of the best procedures to deal with empirical problem, and the way to evaluate scientific information once presented with it.

How can we do that? Before suggesting my solution, let me highlight a further present difficulty that any discussion about the social dimension of science should take into account. A couple of decades ago, some experts of the relationships between science and politics highlighted a problem that sees journalism playing a growing role within the prescriptive credit of political action and shortening this way the temporal perspective of politics itself. Maybe journalism only acted as a catalyzer, but it is true that a peculiar aspect of today's political dynamics are very short-time frames for the appreciation of any decision's practical outcomes. This now represents a compulsory requirement also for science to justify its utility considering its great demand for investments. As a result, financing public bodies became very demanding towards every research project, in terms of applicable outcomes and technological transfers having the task to solve some economic or social problems. However, this condition has threatened scientific authoritativeness under more than one level, including the reliability of internal professional standards.

In other words, the political perception of science is faced with the overwhelming tendency to assign a "normative superiority of the present over the past and the future". This kind of attitude surely facilitates the evaluation of the level of reliability with regard to democratic decision procedures about social and institutional dynamics whose results are rapidly scattered, but on the other hand, they also produce a condition of ahistorical fallacy that culturally impoverishes science and mislead the perception of its epistemological basis. The ahistorical fallacy, which can be seen as a diffused inability to perceive scientific problems within a wide temporal perspective, leading to the understanding of phenomena and a healthy sense of modesty in scientists, has become a chronic condition for scientists and a large part of the population making use of scientific information in different ways.

All of the studies focusing on the comprehension of the reasons for the fall of scientific vocations, the students' inability to understand how to scientifically face a problem plus the poor quality of scientific education, believe this fall to be due to the correlation between scientific education or communication and notions and facts. There is a lack of cognitive tools in order to generate and assess scientific tests and explanations leading to a deeper understanding of the nature and development of scientific knowledge and a constructive participation to scientific communication and issues.

Science's communication and teaching should aim at improving the awareness of young people when they are still in the course of their active cognitive development, that their judgments are 'naturally' biased because of the shortcut heuristics that biological evolution has wired in our brains. Such approach would be of a fundamental importance to provide the useful tools elements to appreciate the liberating value and effectiveness of scientific rationality, that is to say to make emerge a sense of autonomy and self-determination in the individuals.

*University of Rome "Sapienza", Italy;
Co-President, Luca Coscioni Association

Graham Watson*

Investing in research means investing in development

I am always delighted to speak to a public from the Radical Party: their contribution to the political scene is extremely important so I am delighted to be here.

I think this congress has been a huge success in attracting a wide range of knowledgeable speakers from academia, the media and the political world, all of whom have unique insights to offer: it was a great pleasure today to listen to Minister Soria here, and I am sorry that this morning I have missed Janez Potocnik, the Commissioner for Science and Research, because his views on scientific freedom are not only important but also political. If you visit Commissioner's website you may see how he is asked why the European Union funds research, to which he begins his reply so: "New ideas and innovations will help create new jobs. They will help find new methods in protecting the environment, in insuring safer foods and medicines and safer and sustainable energy and resources".

I think nobody here would object to that objective, to those outcomes; the purpose of scientific research should not be simply the ends established by politicians: at best, research operates as a free market, as a place in which scientists produce valuable ideas and into which other people can buy – ideas, inventions, innovations that governments have not encouraged because nobody had dreamt that they were possible. Things come out of the creativity and the inventiveness of the scientific brain. I am convinced that science will flourish and citizens will benefit where scientists are given the resources to expand the boundaries of knowledge and are given the freedom to innovate without political pressure.

However we live in an age where politics sometimes hinder scientific freedom, at least as much as enabling it. Let me take some examples: in the United States of America, science has been under siege and after 9-11 academic freedom and scientific research faced a sustained attack from the Bush administration. Firstly, restrictions on information: the expansion of government classification powers ushered in a reign of secrecy and designation of all areas of research as "sensitive", leading to the withdrawal of thousands of documents from public access and restrictions on thousands more. American publishers were barred from consulting with or editing for researchers who lived in countries like Iran or Cuba, which were subject to trade embargos. We also saw restrictions on scientific materials and technology: the government increased restrictions on products called "select agents" in biomedical or other research. While some government regulation of biological agents may be justified to protect public health and to [prevent] misuses for terrorism, the same agents are often common place, they exist in nature and have everyday uses for scientists, so there must be extreme caution when measures are being taken to ensure that beneficial research is not hindered. I fear that caution was not there in the months after 9-11. We saw science in the United States becoming politicized, with the US administration repeatedly claiming restrictions that were imposed on science and academia albeit unnecessary for protecting national security. The evidence suggests that the administration sought to increase political control over scientific and academic inquiry in order to consolidate its ideological position, for example the White House's exertion of control over scientific peer review, or the stacking of scientific advisory panels with ideologically motivated persons allied to the regime, or the suppression and distortion of scientific and public health information.

I hope that the future looks brighter for scientific research on the other side of the Atlantic. The Obama administration offers a chance to reverse the trend, and I think that the new President has been encouraging positions with regard to stem cell research, among other things. We do not yet know how far he will go, but we do know that there are many vested interests which still seek to stifle research for religious or ideological reasons and that will not be easy to undo. We ought to be pushing the US government to show it can still be the world leader in scientific research, and show them what the implications are of restrictions on freedom of research, which could echo throughout the world.

I wish I could claim that Europe had a great record of freedom in scientific research, and it is true to say that in Europe research has not been stifled to the same degree as a consequence of the same ideological impulse. We cannot imagine that politics play no part in science here, because they do, as my friend Philippe Busquin knows very well having been a Commissioner for Research. There are far too many so-called modern European universities that have superseded intellectual and scientific experimentation with the objective of making students fit for the labour market as soon as possible. In Germany and other countries authorities have been known to put pressure on universities to close departments that do not produce benefits. Too often money is not following research but research is following money, and that is a restriction on scientific freedom. Sometimes governments undermine science by ignoring it in politics. Often, a certain research is set aside in favour of popular politics.

Let me take a couple of examples from the United Kingdom, which may explain it: four years ago, the government agency charged with licensing drugs announced that it would license homeopathic remedies, despite the fact that to make their claims they do not need clinical trial data and peer review research as every modern pharmaceutical does. Unproved remedies are now licensed with their bottles and packets, proclaiming the ailments they are supposed to cure without any clear scientific basis.

This is a subject I feel very strongly about and I could talk about it at length, but you have many other people to listen to this afternoon, so let me conclude by saying that I want to see public money directed to those research projects with defined ends in this time of recession, for example investment in green technology. Take the European super-grid for the production and distribution of renewable energy: you could create a new generation of green jobs, putting Europe on the right side of the green technology path and reducing its dependence on Russia for oil and gas.

However, Europe has a post-war record of under-investment in research and development, and our long-term objective must be to increase the money flow into scientific inquiry, to fund research that is not for economic output or motivated by a political agenda, and to set free the creative genius of science enabling knowledge, discovery, and perhaps benefits that we cannot even imagine today. We currently find ourselves on the downward slope of a recession, precisely the reason for investing more in the knowledge industries that will create the wealth and opportunities of our future. We are talking about a reflection of the economies to the tune of some 20 billion euro; I think we are only scratching the surface of what needs to be done: were we really to build for sustained and long-term growth, we would probably end up investing three or four times that amount. Take the European SuperGrid example: you can create a European SuperGrid powered by solar thermopower and windpower at a cost of 45 billion euro, which is a lot of money but it will save us 250 billion by the year 2050 in addition to other benefits such as bringing people back to work.

I assure you that similar investments would bring similar benefits: sometimes, in normal times, it is hard to find the political will, the determination, the guts and the grit to do the things you want to do; a crisis is precisely the time you need to find it and for the citizens to

appreciate its benefits. I hope that this is the way we will be approaching the crisis, pursuing what a British liberal is pleased to describe as
good, old Keynesian economics: investing in future prosperity and long
term as a way of making sure we come out of this recession in one
piece.

*President, Group of the Alliance of Liberals and Democrats
for Europe in the European Parliament

The ethical, political and legal foundation of freedom of research and teaching

John Harris*
Taking the "human" out of human rights and the "dignity"
out of human dignity and putting the science back

I am delighted to be back, I say back at this congress because I was privileged to participate in the first meeting of this Congress three years ago in Rome. I am honored to be invited back. Obviously I did not entirely disgrace myself on that first occasion, but to make up things I intend to disgrace myself on this occasion. My title is: "Taking the 'human' out of the human rights and the 'dignity' out of human dignity and putting the science back." I have chosen this title because I think that both of these ideas, that is the idea of human rights and the idea of human dignity, are having a deleterious – to put it mildly - effect on the freedom of science research. I should say that this is a work in progress. And I should acknowledge my colleague John Sulston, a Nobel Prize Winner in 2002, who apologizes for not being able to be here today. The paper that I shall present is definitively my own, and not John's; he has no responsibility for most of these ideas.

Human dignity is, I think, a vacuous and discredited concept. It is also inherently speciesist and will very soon be outdated for reasons that I will go into in a moment. Human rights are more respectable, not least because of the universality that has helped to conquer racism and sexism and other arbitrary and vicious forms of discrimination. Unfortunately, as we shall see, the universality of human rights is both too universal and not universal enough. It is therefore, I believe, time to take the "human" out of human rights and the "dignity" out of human dignity. First of all, because it is very probable that in the future there will be no more human beings. This is not necessarily something we should worry about for reasons that I will come onto. Either Darwinian - or more likely a different form of evolution determined by human choices - will – we must hope - put an end to our species, but not, I hope, before it has replaced our species with something better. This process of human enhancement, which was referred to by Philippe Busquin earlier, is already of course dramatically under way. There are many examples. I will mention just two: one is the sort of chemical cognitive enhancement by drugs that

81

are already enabling human beings their academic and cognitive performances. You may have seen a paper of which I was a co-author on the subject which appeared in *Nature* in December. The second reason is because the concept of dignity adds nothing to the force of "human" for those who use the term "human dignity". It simply means "human" with added emphasis. Of course the legitimacy of the emphasis does all the work.

Human rights is one of the most important and universally accepted ideas both in moral and political philosophy and in contemporary jurisprudence. While appeals to human rights are by no means unproblematic, where there is agreement or jurisprudential support for the existence of particular rights, this fact becomes a powerful tool for the protection of such rights and for the remedies that such protection affords. It is a pity then that the insertion of "human" into our concept of rights has occurred so thoughtlessly and with such little attention to the prejudice embodied in this idea.

A deep question, and one that serves to gloss the claims just made, is: what role does "humanity" – species membership, being a human being, in short the descriptive sense of being human - play in our evaluative use of that term? When we identify humanity not simply with species membership - being a human being - but with being a moral being, we may be claiming one of two very different things. The first is that we humans, the species *homo sapiens sapiens*, is characterised by, among other qualities, moral agency and other important features like the capacities for sympathy, empathy and creativity. The second implies more: that the possession of these qualities is essentially human, possessed by us only because we are the species that we are. This second sense implies that our humanity in the moral sense is not simply species-typical, but rather it requires being human in the biological or genetic sense. There is not only a danger, there is a long established and deeply ingrained habit, of identifying properties or qualities that are contingently possessed by human beings as necessarily possessed by our kind and, moreover, necessarily not possessed by other kinds.

When we ask questions like: "What is it to be human?", or talk about a person's "humanity" or talk of the "human spirit" or "human values," we not only emphasise the properties that typically distinguish our species from species, we indulge in a sort of chauvinism, celebrating our own kind as we do in a different sense when we talk of "Britishness", "European culture" or "Western civilization". Many of you recall, I believe, an apocryphal story about Mahatma Ghandi who, after a visit to London after the start of the Second World War, was asked by a journalist what he thought of Western civilization and he famously responded: "I think it would be a very good thing".

This human chauvinism is often given a pseudo-scientific bent which is inimical to both the spirit of science and indeed to free inquiry. There is often talk of species barriers as if, in so far as such things exist, they are laws of nature set up not simply to protect our supposed species purity, but to preserve those qualities we possess that other creatures allegedly do not and - the implication is - could not, because they are not human. A number of recent developments in biotechnology and in our understanding of evolution indicate that the time has come not only for a reassessment of the role of the term "human" in human rights but of the idea of "humanity" in our conceptions of ourselves and of our place in the universe.

Humanimals. The possibility of there-existing part human – part animal creatures seems always to have fascinated human beings. Centaurs and mermaids are just two familiar examples. In our own times the possibility of deliberately creating such creatures has for the first time become a reality and the prospect fascinates and excites as well as causing horror and loathing. But most importantly it offers immense promise for the treatment of disease and for the amelioration and enhancement of the human condition. While the prospect of mixing species exercises both popular and scientific imagination in different ways, the ethics and the permissibility of creating hybrids, chimeras and other forms of novel combinations of cells, with some human and some animal elements, has become one of the most urgent ethical problems facing contemporary science. This is because it has become obvious that not only can we learn much from the creation of such potentially ambiguous entities, but the therapeutic prospects, the chance to use what we learn to treat and prevent disease and to understand much more about ourselves and indeed about animals, are generally believed to be enormous.

In this discussion I use the term "humanimal" to cover any biological entities, whether individual creatures or indeed cells, which have any mixture of animal and human elements. Humanimals of course have been created for many years, and hybrids have almost certainly always existed naturally. However, the ethics of their creation and use is still in its infancy. A recent report by the United Kingdom Academy of Medical Sciences identifies many aspects of basic science that have been and continue to be studied in ways which involve the "mixing" of animal and human derived cells. This was a report called *Embryo Species* and published in 2007. I was in the Academy Working Party that produced that report. The ethical question is whether the sanctity of so-called species barriers - or other objections to inter-species constructs - affords good or even plausible reasons to abandon such research and forego or postpone whatever benefits it might yield.

The Mermaid's Myth. A very important question is: "How do we identify tissue or genes as animal or human?". From diet to vaccines, from drugs to xeno-transplantation in its various forms, as Giuseppe Testa has noted: "Humans and animals have always been exchanging bits of their biological matter, intentionally or by chance, naturally or through artificial aids of various sorts". It is worth remembering that the majority of these encounters do not elicit particular fear or opposition. Diet is a good example, except for vegetarians for whom objections to eating animals are usually rooted in moral issues concerning animal welfare rather than species mixing, there does not seem to be any preoccupation with the entry of animal genes, cells, tissue, muscle and other bodily products into our daily metabolism. However we know and we learn more almost on a daily basis, that diet influences our body at both genetic and epigenetic levels. The effect of certain classes of nutrients on the methylation level of our DNA - one of the most meaningful types of epigenetic modification - is just the best defined example of the enduring effect of diet on our genetic networks, an effect that might even be passed on to future generations. In fact, if one were consistent in maximizing the purity of human matter, the only dietary choice would be cannibalism, rather than eating animals for food.

Vaccines and the various kinds of xeno-transplantation are other, more visible, instances of animal-human mixing. Although whole organ xeno-transplantations are still in very experimental phases, porcine neural stem cells have been transplanted into a few patients and millions of patients worldwide live with heart valves harvested from pigs or cows. In such cases, objections have tended to concentrate on specific dangers - for example the risk of transmitting animal viruses to the human population - rather than on a more general condemnation of human-animal mixing. A typology of different modalities of human-animal mixing emerges:

- The daily crossing of species boundaries through diet, largely unnoticed and completely normalized in our culture;
- the widespread use of animal products of various kinds as medical remedies, usually well accepted though with specific safety concerns, as in the various kinds of xeno-transplantation and indeed vaccines;

- the mixing of human and animal genes as proposed, albeit at a very limited level, in research. And finally
- the possibility of fully fledged hybrid or chimerical creatures mixing human and animal elements.

Should we retain a very great suspicion of this latter possibility? We should say some more about what it might mean to mix human and animal parts in a way that would resort in a creature that runs around on the carpet and frightens the horses. It does not follow that an animal gene once put into a human, behaves as an independent unit of 'animal agency' or vice versa. And a clear reminder of this point comes from some of the most spectacular results of molecular biology in the 1990s. In the mid-90s, scientists defined the genetic hierarchy underlying the development of the eye. The experiment was spectacular and the very wording in which we still describe its outcome - genetic hierarchy - is a legacy of its seminal character: "A single gene was transplanted in tissues of the fly embryo such as the wings and the legs and was able to direct the formation of a whole eye, an ectopic eye. And yet, when the human homolog gene was transferred into a mouse to check for its ability to repair the small eye mutation, the result remained compelling - again, an eye was formed, testifying to the remarkable evolutionary conservation of genes and developmental pathways". But the eye formed from a human gene, when inserted into the mouse 'forms' a mouse eye, not a human eye. Context, in other words, is vital. We are obsessed by the mermaids' myth. We expect human and animal mixing to result in creatures that are mixtures of typical or phenotypical features of those species. This is not necessarily the case. We, humans are already humanimals. We know we are descended from apes, but we perhaps need to remind ourselves that this descent is seamless and means that our genetic constitution contains a mixture of the genes of all the creatures, all the other species, that are part of the origin of our transient and transitional species.

I would like to remind you of a wonderful illustration in an essay by my colleague Richard Dawkins called *Gaps in the Mind*. He suggests to conduct a thought experiment. He asks us to imagine a contemporary woman, holding her mother's hand on the coast of Africa. She holds her mother's hand, her mother holds her mother's and so on. Each daughter is as much like her mother as daughters usually are. Each person takes up a about a meter, a yard, of space as they hold hands back into the past. In just 300 miles - a small distance into Africa - the imaginary human chain reaches our common ape ancestor. We then need to imagine our ape ancestor holding by her other hand her other daughter and she hers and so on, back to the coast. Again each daughter looks as much like her mother as mothers and daughters usually do. By the time the chain reaches back to the coast two contemporary females are looking at one another, each holding the hand of her mother stretching in seamless connection back to a common ape ancestor. The two - women shall we call them - looking into each other's eyes are a modern human and a modern chimpanzee.

Dawkins's story is a salutary reminder of our ape ancestry and most importantly of the seamlessness of our connection with our apes ancestors. We need to bear in mind another lesson from evolution related to Dawkins's parable and outlined in his essay. That lesson is that it is an accident of evolution that ape species, with whom - which? - we humans might have been able - successfully - to breed, have not survived. So, while the chimpanzee who shares a common ancestor with humans probably cannot breed with human beings - at least without technological assistance - there were certainly once non-human apes that, had they survived, could have been procreational partners for us, using "normal" sexual reproduction. To this extent our ability to define ourselves as a species distinct from the other great apes is - in one of the most commonly used definitions of a species, namely - that its members are able to breed successfully with one another, but not with other types of animals. An accident of history. It might not have been like that. It certainly was not. It is important for us to remember this seamlessness. If we have horror of human-animal mixing, it is misplaced. We ourselves, all of us, are such mixtures. And with the aid of technology we could also - if we wanted to, there would not be much point - reproduce with animals.

The last point. I would like to go back to my first point that in the future there will be no more human beings. Evolution has left us with a very mixed constitutional blessing. We heard this morning from Charles (Sabine). That in the future there will be no more human beings. Evolution has left us with a very mixed constitutional blessing. We heard this morning from Charles, how mixed blessing it is. We are vulnerable and subject to premature death of horrific sorts. I hope we can do better than this. And if we are to survive, we will have to do better than that. If we influence evolution and we start to build immunities to this sort of conditions into the human genome, we would not only have showed that the UNESCO ridiculous remarks of some years ago that we ought to preserve the human genome as the common heritage of humanity is an absurdity, but we would also have opened the door to a future that actually may mean that intelligent creatures capable of pursuing science might be able to continue to exist on this planet. Even if they are not human.

*Bioethics, University of Manchester, United Kingdom

Dick Taverne*
Freedom of research and eco-fundamentalism

I want to start with two apologies. This afternoon's is the only session I can attend. Having heard this session, it is clear that I have missed a great deal, because the contributions I have heard are extremely valuable and important.

My second apology is that I am going to talk about an important aspect of science, but I am not a scientist. As a student I studied Philosophy and Ancient History. The only time I came close to a scientific education was on a debating tour of American colleges, when I was asked what I majored in. I said: "Classics". And either because of my accent, or the unfamiliarity of the subject in that college, I was introduced as "Dick Taverne who majors in Plastics."

However, I am married to a biologist and I have become increasingly concerned with public ignorance of science. When someone says: "I know nothing about science", it is often not an admission, but a boast. I agree with what Mrs. Bonino has said: there is a great deal of hostility towards science, in Britain as well as Italy. So about seven years ago, I founded a charity, *Sense about Science*, to fight this hostility. Its main aim is to promote the evidence-based approach to scientific issues. We have 3,000 eminent scientists who work with us to counteract the anti-science mood.

One other point: I am a politician, an ex-member of Parliament and now member of a very strange institution, the British Upper House, the House of Lords. We are appointed by an independent commission, on the basis of past contributions to society or special expertise. And we are appointed for life. That has disadvantages and advantages. It does mean that a few of our members who were appointed for life, have become quite old. When I arrived first, I was astonished to find many eminent figures from the past, former Secretaries of State for example, from so long ago I thought they were dead. And there they were making speeches. It is a kind of proof there is life after death. But being appointed for life also has an important advantage. You cannot be sacked. I am not responsible to electors. I can be as outrageous as I like and no one can hold me to task. And some things I shall say this afternoon will be somewhat provocative.

We have heard today about the threat to religious freedom from fundamentalism. My topic is agricultural research. I am concerned with the opposition to genetically modified crops. It is one of the key battlefields of science versus anti-science. It is also under threat, not from religious fundamentalism, but from eco-fundamentalism.

Let me start with certain general observations. I am an admirer of that glorious episode in mankind's history, the Enlightenment. It was not only the birth of modern science, but also the occasion of the first steps towards democracy. Like the philosopher Karl Popper, I believe the two are linked. Science depends on the criticism of ideas. It is inconsistent with autocracy. Secondly, science is tentative knowledge and therefore opposed to dogma. And thirdly, science is the enemy of prejudice and ignorance and intolerance, which have always been the basis for the denial of human rights. Racism, chauvinism and the suppression of women's rights, were all based on prejudice and ignorance of the characteristics of different races, nations and genders. One example of dogma and unreason today is the opposition, which is particularly common in Europe, to the cultivation of genetically modified crops.

Let me start by asking: what are the benefits and risks of GM crops? And why is the opposition to them a threat to freedom? Outside Europe, GM crops are a huge success. Over 125 million hectares are cultivated by GM crops. The area on which they are grown increases by more than 10% a year and mainly in the developing world. They have already produced considerable benefits. Over 11 million small-scale farmers now grow genetically modified cotton, mainly in India and China. They have increased their incomes substantially, because they have lower costs. They do not have to buy so many pesticides and their health is improved, because they do not have to spray so often.

The idea that GM crops only benefit big multinationals is mistaken. Most of the development is taking place in the third world. Not only do GM crops reduce poverty, but also improve the environment, contrary to what is claimed by the opponents, because they have lessened the use of pesticides. They have promoted no-till farming, avoiding the need to plough. This preserves the top soil and no longer disturbs birds nests. It also uses less energy. A very carefully peer-reviewed paper in 2007 demonstrated that the benefits of GM crops to the environment were the equivalent of taking 4 million cars off the road. And there will be a large number of important environmental developments in the future, like GM crops that can grow in crops in arid regions or salty soil. They will also provide enormous benefits to health. Perhaps the best example is so-called golden rice, which can help to supply the vitamin A deficiency that causes half a million children to go blind and causes two million deaths a year. Other products are in the pipeline, such as edible vaccines from bananas and tomatoes, which can have hugely beneficial effects on human health

But what about the risks? Opponents claim that there is a risk to human health. However, every national academy of sciences in the world, the Third World academy of sciences, the Brazilian, American, the Mexican academies, the British Royal Society have all concluded that there is not a shred of evidence of harm to people or environment. Americans have been eating food with a GM content for something like 12 years. And there has not been a single law case. When American lawyers do not find ground to sue, there must be something going right.

Why is there this opposition? And how is it a threat to research freedom? The opposition is a kind of religion. It is a form of eco-fundamentalism, because Greenpeace and Friends of the Earth, who lead it, ignore the evidence on dogmatic grounds. They ignore the evidence of the FAO and the WHO. And they use every means to suppress GM crops.

Some argue that genetic modification is playing God with nature and seek to prevent research that interferes with nature. Prince Charles is an exponent of the view that we must not play God with nature. Yet biotechnology is as old as the hills. What have farmers always done with nature? To grow better crops and plants. What is that, but interference with nature? In Britain, the director of Greenpeace was asked in evidence to a House of Lords committee: "Is there anything which could change your mind? What if there was evidence that came to light that proved that GM crops are safe? Would you abandon your opposition?". "No" he said. It is definite and permanent and complete opposition. Nothing would change his mind. It was just like the Pope's representative who was asked by Galileo to look at a new planet and said: "I refuse to look at a planet that my religion tells me cannot exist".

Instead of accepting evidence, opponents go for ill-founded scare stories. There was the story about Monarch butterflies, which were supposed to be harmed by a pollen from GM maize. Heavy sprinkling of this pollen on milk-wood leaves in a laboratory was shown to harm the larvae of the butterflies. But in later field trials, the pollen had no effect on the butterfly larvae at all. In the years when the cultivation of GM maize was growing strongly, the total population of butterflies actually increased. Another scare was that the failure of GM cotton was causing massive suicides of farmers in India. In fact India has seen the fastest growth in the cultivation of GM cotton anywhere in the world. When the scare story was examined very carefully by the International Food Policy Research Institute, they found no evidence to support it. Suicides of farmers had gone down. Cotton cultivation had increased. There was no link between them.

In the case of some crops which have huge potential and benefit, like golden rice, Greenpeace and Friends of the Earth have done everything they can to slow down or prevent their development. They deny despite the evidence that golden rice can produce any benefits. But how does this affect the freedom of research? It affects it in three ways: through crop destruction, overregulation and stirring up public opinion.

As far as crop destruction is concerned, this has occurred frequently in France, England, Germany and elsewhere. The opponents do not confine themselves to argument, but believe in action. They have forced farmers to stop their land being used for experiments. Universities have been intimidated. Two German universities banned crop trials, because some had been damaged by vandals. The president of one university said: "We are no longer able to deal with the massive opposition. The University has a reputation we cannot risk losing". It is odd that an university says it can only maintain its reputation by stopping academic research because of blackmail. These crop-burners are the modern equivalent of the book burners or witch hunters. They destroy the evidence before it can be shown whether it actually causes harm.

The next way in which freedom of research is affected is through overregulation. Because of the activities of the opponents and the scares spread about GM crops, regulations have made it 10 to 20 times more expensive to produce a new GM crop than the equivalent (and probably inferior) conventionally-grown crop. Regulation is based on process, not on what it should be: product. In fact, the process of genetic modification, which is much more heavily regulated, is more targeted, quicker and more efficient. It leads to less random and less unexpected results than conventional breeding. Most conventional breeding of new plants to produce mutations is done by bombarding seeds with gamma rays, which is very much a hit-and-miss process. If the public knew about that, they might be rather scared. Radiation has special connotations, even though plant irradiation is in fact perfectly safe.

As a result of the special regulation to which new GM plants are subject, it is far more expensive and takes far longer to produce GM crops than conventional ones. The result is oligopoly. Most universities and publicly funded research cannot afford the extra delays and expense. Nor can small companies. That is why golden rice has been held up amongst other reasons. And thank God for Bill Gates, who announced 47 million dollar program for developing new GM staple crops in Africa.

When it comes to GM, I am afraid the EU record is depressing. The only crop that is commercially grown on any scale is maize in Spain. In France GM maize was very popular with farmers and the area on which it was cultivated was growing at the astonishing rate of 5 to 10 times a year. Then the president banned its further growth. There is a ban on the import of GM maize in France, Austria, Hungary and Greece, contrary to all the scientific advice they have received.

If I may conclude, these restrictions are a serious threat to freedom. In Europe we do not give in to religious fundamentalism in general and we denounce intolerance. But we treat Greenpeace as heroes. A lot of their campaigns I fully support. But they have starved Africa of science and with disastrous results they have persuaded African governments they should go for traditional, not the latest scientific farming. In Europe they have virtually banned GM crops. We do not decide policy issues in other fields on illfounded scare stories not based on evidence. In the case of GM we do.

The Chinese are now the leaders in the research and development of agricultural biotechnology. They regard it as one of the most important technologies of the future, essential for the avoidance of hunger and poverty. They can do these experiments. And we cannot. Which would you expect to be the countries that promote freedom for research? Europe or China? The place where freedom is restricted is Europe. In China it is free.

*Founder, Sense about Science;
member, House of Lords Science and Technology Committee,
United Kingdom

Mark B. Brown*
What does it mean to have a right to research?

This conference seems to have two basic aims: to advocate scientific freedom, and to think critically about what scientific freedom means. As a matter of advocacy, I fully agree with the conference organizers that scientific freedom is important and needs to be defended against ideological restrictions. But in this talk, I want to focus on the second task of considering what it means to have scientific freedom and a right to research. Freedom does not have a single meaning, and unless we think carefully about different meanings of freedom, we risk advocating a kind of scientific freedom that ultimately undermines itself.

There are at least three traditions of thinking about freedom in Western societies. The first is the standard liberal view, which political theorists associate with Thomas Hobbes. This view sees freedom as a matter of freedom from interference. This is the most common way of conceiving scientific freedom today. For example, in the United States in November 2004, the voters of California passed Proposition 71, which established three billion dollars in public funding for stem cell research. This proposition also amended the California State Constitution to include "a right to conduct stem cell research". The sponsors were responding to the ideological policies of the Bush administration, and they presented Prop. 71 as a way of protecting stem cell research from political interference. They assumed that it would provide a barrier against government interference with science. What actually happened, however, is that Prop. 71 led to years of legal and political controversy. As soon as it passed, it was challenged by two lawsuits, and the newly created stem cell institute was widely criticized for nepotism and the misuse of public funds. The state legislature has repeatedly tried to require more transparency in the distribution of public funds for stem cell research. In short, Prop. 71 did not keep politics out of science. It became a political issue itself.

The California experience with Prop. 71 suggests at least two problems with the standard liberal view of scientific freedom. First, by attempting to isolate science from society, the standard liberal view conveys an image of science as pure and value-free. This image conflicts with empirical studies of science, especially in applied areas like biomedicine, which shows how science is intertwined with social and political values. Second, the standard liberal view of scientific freedom implicitly promotes the politicization of science. It does this by suggesting that scientific knowledge should lead directly and necessarily to particular policies. For example, defenders of scientific freedom often argue that because science promises cures for disease, it should be both free of political restrictions and generously funded. I happen to agree that science does promise cures for many terrible diseases, and that it should be generously funded. But many other worthy projects also require government funding, and there is never enough money to go around. This means that political decisions require difficult comparisons and trade-offs between competing goals. The standard liberal view of scientific freedom is not prepared to undertake such comparisons, because it isolates science from society. What often happens instead is that advocates of scientific freedom feel pressured to exaggerate the short-term promise of science and to suggest that medical cures are just around the corner. In this way, science becomes politicized. And when the public realizes that the promises were exaggerated, scientific freedom seems to be nothing more than a way to promote the self-interest of scientists. Scientific freedom gets reduced to interest-group politics.

A similar problem occurs when people defend scientific freedom with reference to free-market principles. Some have argued that science is like an economic market, because in each case government interference supposedly distorts incentives and hinders growth. Governments cannot pick winners in the marketplace, the argument goes, and they also cannot pick winners among scientists. Although there is something to be said for this argument, it ultimately poses a threat to scientific freedom. It encourages a view of scientists as private entrepreneurs, concerned with nothing more than their own careers. It also reinforces the current trend toward the commercialization of science. In many fields today, private funding of science is much higher than public funding. And the restrictions imposed by private corporations often pose a greater threat to scientific freedom than restrictions imposed by governments. In democratic societies, government restrictions are at least open to public criticism and revision through the political process. It is more difficult to challenge the restrictions on public disclosure and licensing contained in many corporate research contracts. If efforts to resist the politicization of science implicitly support the commercialization of science, they will end up throwing scientists from the frying pan into the fire. This becomes a serious risk when scientific freedom is defended in terms of the standard liberal conception of freedom.

A second view of freedom can be traced back to Aristotle and Rousseau. This communitarian view sees freedom as a matter of freedom through collective self-government. I do not want to discuss this view today, except to say that I think it also tends to threaten scientific freedom. The communitarian view tends to suppress political disagreements in favor of social consensus, and it easily leads to paternalistic policies and ideological restrictions on science.

A third view of freedom that I find more promising is that found in the republican tradition associated with Machiavelli. According to republicans, freedom is freedom from domination. That is to say, the key threat to freedom is not interference as such, but unjustified and arbitrary interference. This view of freedom recognizes that some forms of interference actually enhance freedom. A traffic light, for example, certainly interferes with automobile drivers, but by preventing accidents it enhances their freedom. In the same way, government restrictions on research with human subjects, or restrictions on the use of hazardous materials, enhance scientific freedom by increasing public confidence in science. In some cases it may be better for scientists to establish such restrictions themselves, rather than government. But in many cases, governments are better able to enforce restrictions that benefit science. Scientists alone, for example, would have a difficult time prosecuting and punishing criminal activity in the laboratory. Moreover, when beneficial restrictions are imposed by governments, they are open to public deliberation and debate. Although scientists tend to perceive public deliberation about science as a threat, it has the potential to increase public support for science. Citizens are more likely to accept public funding for science, when they have some say in how their tax monies are spent. In sum, the republican view says that government restrictions may enhance scientific freedom, if they are publicly justified and revisable through a democratic process.

Now, scientist's main concern today, of course, is not with restrictions on human subjects research or hazardous materials, but on stem cell research and other areas that are morally controversial. In opposition to such restrictions, scientists often claim a right to research. In English and several other languages, the word right comes from the Latin *rectus*, meaning "straight". When applied to human affairs, the word "right" originally referred to an objective standard of conduct. To do something "rightly" meant to do it "correctly". By the seventeenth century, the meaning had changed. A right began to refer, not to something being right, but to the notion that people have rights. The idea of doing something that is right changed into the idea of doing something because one has a right to do it. The notion of right referred, not to an objective standard, but to property in oneself that offers protection from the social order. The idea of self-possession implied rights to life, liberty, bodily safety, speech, religion, and so on. This new concept of right retained aspects of the older view, because rights were conceived as natural and, therefore, prior to society and politics. Within this history, however, there have been two distinct concepts of rights, and they each have very different implications for scientific freedom.

The more common view of rights builds on the liberal conception of freedom. The liberal view of rights sees them as natural individual protections against interference by society and the state. During the Enlightenment, this notion of rights played a key role in the struggle against absolutism and the rise of liberal democracy. It has become nearly synonymous with liberalism, even though some prominent liberals, such as Jeremy Bentham and John Stuart Mill, did not share the idea of rights as prior to politics.

Recent claims for a "right to research" have usually been phrased in the liberal protective language of natural rights. I already mentioned some of the problems this created with California's Prop. 71. To some extent, however, it makes perfect sense to think of a right to research as a negative right against State inference. Almost nobody claims that the right to research provides a positive right to the means for conducing research. Even if governments have a duty to promote research in general, most people recognize that governments cannot fund all promising research. In this sense, the issue is a matter of what government may prevent, not what it must promote.

But the right to research is not properly understood as a fundamental right or a basic human right. The right to research is not like the right to free expression or the free exercise of religion. Conducing scientific research is not a requirement of basic human dignity. Nor is conducing research necessary for human fulfillment. A close look at some of the leading international human rights declarations supports this view. For example, the United Nations Universal Declaration of Human Rights lists rights to basic education, fairly paid work, a standard of living adequate for health and well-being, and even rest and leisure – but it does not mention a right to research. To be sure, Article 27 recognizes a right to copyright and patent protection – that is, a right to the benefits resulting from scientific, literary, or artistic production. It also mentions a right "to share in scientific advancement and its benefits". But a right to enjoy the products of science is not the same as a right to produce science.

The same is true of the UNESCO Universal Declaration on the Human Genome and Human Rights. Article 12(b) does mention that "freedom of research, which is necessary for the progress of knowledge, is part of freedom of thought". And articles 14 and 15 encourage governments to promote research. But these same articles also make clear that governments should "consider the ethical, legal, social and economic implications of such research", and that research should "safeguard respect for human rights, fundamental freedoms and human dignity and... protect public health". It seems fair to conclude that these declarations do not portray the right to research as a fundamental human right.

This makes sense, when one considers that not all people are capable, even in principle, of enjoying a right to research. Not everyone is capable of doing the sort of advanced scientific work that advocates of a right to research want to defend. Indeed, many defenders of scientific freedom seem to be thinking not of a right to research, but rather the rights of researchers. They do not mean to defend a general right to do research that applies to everyone. Of course, the rights of researchers need to be defended. But it may be helpful to recognize that because the right to research cannot include everyone, its moral force is more limited than other more basic rights.

In sum, when conceived as an individual protection, the right to research draws a boundary between science and politics. It asserts a quasi-private sphere within which the political community has no jurisdiction. But by isolating science from society, this view of the right to research ultimately does more to threaten science than protect it.

Fortunately, the liberal view of rights has long co-existed with a different view, which I will call the republican view of rights. For republicans, rights are claims to civic membership. The republican view emphasizes the link between individual rights and human equality, which is what gives rights their moral force: my claim to have a right to something is only persuasive, if I recognize that you are entitled to make the same claim. That is why masters do not demand that slaves recognize their rights. And slaves who demand rights assert their equality with the masters. In this respect, the phrase "equal rights" is redundant. Although most people today conceive rights in the liberal mode as natural protections against society and government, in practice the republican view of rights is what has given rights their real power. Rights have acquired moral force only through political struggles for equality. Whether or not rights actually are "natural", historically rights have only become effective when they are brought to life in political culture. The rights of workers, women, minorities, and other groups have been promoted not primarily through philosophical claims, but through political arguments and popular mobilization. When these groups demanded rights, they demanded to be fully included in society. In the same way, the republican view of the right to research argues for the inclusion of science within the political community. The right to research becomes a particular instance of a more general right to inquiry that all citizens share. Non-scientists are more likely to accept a right to research, if it is also linked to corresponding obligations. If ordinary citizens have an obligation to fight disease by promoting science, as John Harris has argued, scientists may have an obligation to support democracy by engaging in politics. Unless scientists begin to see the right to research as a claim to membership in society, non-scientists have little reason to grant them the freedom (and public funding) they need. To put this somewhat differently, the republican view sees the right to research not as a right against the democratic process, but as part of the democratic process. Here it may be helpful to distinguish among three sorts of rights:

- *political rights* - such as freedom of speech and assembly - which are integral to democracy
- *social rights* - such as basic education and health care - which are a precondition for democracy
- *civil rights* - such as religious liberty, property, and privacy - which are external to the democratic process, but generally supportive of democratic culture.

The right to research may take any of these forms, but which form it takes will affect the degree of protection it deserves. Generally speaking, civil rights are more subject to restriction than social and political rights, because social and political rights are required for citizens to manage their disagreements about all rights. Any restrictions on social and political rights are difficult to revise, since they limit the process of revision itself.

It makes sense to include inquiry - as distinct from the more narrow category of scientific research - in the scope of political rights that are integral to the democratic process. The most obvious reason is that democracy requires an informed citizenry. If citizens are not free to conduct inquiries of various kinds, democracy becomes the rule of ignorance. Freedom of the press, for example, is crucial for democracy. Other sorts of inquiry are also important, but they may contribute less directly to democracy than freedom of the press. This has been the view of United States courts, in any case, which have created a hierarchy that prefers political speech and publication to commercial speech and publication, and both to pornography.

This framework may be used to distinguish different levels of protection for different kinds of scientific research. When scientific inquiries produce knowledge necessary for democratic governance, they deserve more protection than when they do not. Scientific research that promotes public health and economic growth also deserves protection, but it deserves protection as a social right, not as a political one. And research pursued for the sake of curiosity deserves protection as a civil right, but it may deserve less protection than research that contributes more directly to democracy.

Of course, these categories are somewhat artificial, and many areas of research fit into more than one category. Also, given the unpredictability of science, the democratic significance of research often changes over time, so its claim to protection may change as well. Nonetheless, this framework offers a heuristic for thinking about how claims for a right to research may support rather than undermine democratic processes.

Finding a mutually supporting relationship between science and democracy is important for at least three reasons. First, democracy has been better for science than other kinds of political systems. And despite its many flaws, democracy has also been better for individual rights than other political systems. In this respect, asserting a right to research against the democratic process risks killing the goose that lays the gold eggs for science. It is no accident that religious fundamentalists attack both scientific freedom and liberal individualism. If we want to effectively counteract these attacks, it will not be enough to simply reassert liberal principles. That just leads to a shouting match. Instead we need to acknowledge the limits of liberalism, and improve the relationship between science and democracy.

Second, even if scientists enjoy extensive rights to research, democratic processes are required for generating public acceptance for their research. Although asserting a right to research may protect scientists from public interference, it does not establish that any particular line of research is in fact worth pursuing. Rights protect choices; they do not guide choices. In this respect, asserting a right to research should not be used to avoid public deliberation on what kinds of research governments should restrict or promote. Instead, asserting a right to research should be the starting point of public deliberation.

Third, asserting a right to research is not the most effective barrier to public restrictions on science. There are many other ways of restraining misguided politicians besides making claims about rights.

In particular, rights claims are most effective when their proponents avoid the temptation to escape politics. The best way to protect the right to research is to combine talk about rights with efforts to generate the popular support that give rights their real power. And that, I hope, is precisely what this conference will achieve.

*Research Associate,
Bielefeld Graduate School in History and Sociology,
Bielefeld University, Germany

Barbara Forrest*
Restoring the Enlightenment: the foundation of American and European science and education

On January 20th, 2009, in his inaugural speech, President Barack Obama assured the American people: "We will restore science to its rightful place". Why was it necessary for Obama to say this to his fellow Americans? It was necessary because, during the presidency of George W. Bush, science - indeed, virtually the entire legacy of the Enlightenment - was directly attacked by the United States government.

America owes a tremendous debt to Europe for the gift of the Enlightenment, which is gratefully acknowledged by most educated Americans. Drawing from its intellectual riches, the founders crafted the constitutional pillars of American democracy, namely, the separation of Church and State and the personal freedoms of speech, the press, and peaceable assembly, all of which protect scientific inquiry. However, for almost fifty years, both have been attacked by creationists operating as part of the broad coalition known as the Religious Right. Although they are not yet as troublesome as in America, European creationists have also made surprising inroads. Partly because of the steady encroachments of creationists, the legacy of the Enlightenment requires protection, if not outright restoration. Scientists and other academics in America and in the areas of Europe where creationists are active must help in this restoration by incorporating the defense of science into a revitalized commitment to civic engagement as citizens of our respective countries.

America's founders understood well their intellectual and political debts to their European kinsmen. For the intellectual defense of religious tolerance and representative government, they were indebted most importantly to John Locke. In seeking to understand the natural world and to improve the quality of life, they built on the work of Bacon, Newton, and others. In George Washington's *Circular to the States*, which he wrote in 1783 to the governors of the thirteen new American States upon leaving his post as commander of the Continental Army, Washington revealed an awareness of how the

Enlightenment had shaped his new country:

> *"The foundation of our Empire was not laid in the gloomy age of Ignorance and Superstition, but at an Epocha when the rights of mankind were better understood and more clearly defined, than at any former period, the researches of the human mind, after social happiness, have been carried to a great extent, the Treasures of knowledge, acquired by the labors of Philosophers, Sages and Legislatures, through a long succession of years, are laid open for our use, and their collected wisdom may be happily applied in the Establishment of our forms of Government; the free cultivation of Letters, the unbounded extension of Commerce, the progressive refinement of Manners, the growing liberality of sentiment, and above all, the pure and benign light of Revelation, have had a meliorating influence on mankind and increased the blessings of Society. At this auspicious period, the United States came into existence as a Nation, and if their Citizens should not be completely free and happy, the fault will be [entirely] their own. Such is our situation, and such are our prospects".*

However, some Americans and Europeans, then as now, saw the Enlightenment as a threat to the traditions and institutions in which their lives were grounded. During the 1800 presidential election, angry clerics attacked Thomas Jefferson as the "Virginia Voltaire" because of his championship of Church-State separation. In 1832, Pope Gregory XVI denounced both the growing demand for intellectual freedom in Europe and the support for the separation of Church and State that threatened Catholic authority. In his encyclical, *Mirari Vos: On Liberalism and Religious Indifferentism,* he bemoaned the popular appeal of the Enlightenment and the growing rejection of the Church's theocratic ambitions. In an encyclical addressed to "all Patriarchs, Primates, Archbishops, and Bishops of the Catholic World," he wrote:

> *"We speak of the things which you see with your own eyes, which We both bemoan. Depravity exults; science is impudent; liberty, dissolute. The holiness of the sacred is despised; the majesty of divine worship is not only disapproved by evil men, but defiled and held up to ridicule. The divine authority of the Church is opposed and her rights shorn off. She is subjected to human reason and with the greatest injustice exposed to the hatred of the people and reduced to vile servitude. The obedience due to bishops is denied and their rights are trampled underfoot. Furthermore, academies and schools resound with new, monstrous opinions, which openly attack the Catholic faith. Thus, by institutions and by the example of teachers,*

the minds of the youth are corrupted and a tremendous blow is dealt to religion and the perversion of morals is spread. So the restraints of religion are thrown off, by which alone kingdoms stand.

"This shameful font of indifferentism gives rise to that absurd and erroneous proposition which claims that liberty of conscience must be maintained for everyone. It spreads ruin in sacred and civil affairs, though some repeat over and over again with the greatest impudence that some advantage accrues to religion from it. Experience shows, even from earliest times, that cities renowned for wealth, dominion, and glory perished as a result of this single evil, namely immoderate freedom of opinion, license of free speech, and desire for novelty.

"Here We must include that harmful and never sufficiently denounced freedom to publish any writings whatever and disseminate them to the people, which some dare to demand and promote with so great a clamor. We are horrified to see what monstrous doctrines and prodigious errors are disseminated far and wide in countless books, pamphlets, and other writings which, though small in weight, are very great in malice.

"The Church has always taken action to destroy the plague of bad books. This was true even in apostolic times for We read that the apostles themselves burned a large number of books. "We must fight valiantly," Clement XIII says in an encyclical letter about the banning of bad books, "as much as the matter itself demands and must exterminate the deadly poison of so many books; for never will the material for error be withdrawn, unless the criminal sources of depravity perish in flames." Thus it is evident that this Holy See has always striven, throughout the ages, to condemn and to remove suspect and harmful books.

"We have learned that certain teachings are being spread among the common people in writings which attack the trust and submission due to princes; the torches of treason are being lit everywhere.

"Nor can We predict happier times for religion and government from the plans of those who desire vehemently to separate the Church from the state, and to break the mutual concord between temporal authority and the priesthood. It is certain that that concord which always was favorable and beneficial for the sacred and the civil order is feared by the shameless lovers of liberty."

The Enlightenment clearly had not influenced Gregory XVI; for him, it was an enemy to be defeated. Ironically, twelve years later, in Philadelphia, Pennsylvania, Catholic parents objected to their children being forced to read the Protestant Bible in city schools and sought redress from public officials. In response to their appeals, Catholics were murdered and their homes and churches burned by Protestant mobs in the Philadelphia Bible Riots of 1844.

Twenty-first-century creationists view the Enlightenment in much the same way as Gregory XVI. There is no better example than the Intelligent Design (ID) creationist movement in the United States. The ID movement - the most aggressive, troublesome form of American creationism - operates from the Discovery Institute, a conservative think tank in Seattle, Washington. William Dembski, a mathematician and philosopher who is the movement's chief intellectual and one of its most prominent spokesmen, explicitly attacks the Enlightenment in a book for his lay audience of ID supporters. In *Intelligent Design: The Bridge Between Science and Theology*, Dembski predicts the Enlightenment's demise:

"The question is how we should do science and theology in light of the impending collapse of Enlightenment rationalism and scientific naturalism. These ideologies are on their way out not because they are false (although they are that) but because they are bankrupt.

"The scientific picture of the world championed since the Enlightenment is not just wrong but massively wrong. Indeed entire fields of inquiry, especially in the human sciences, will need to be rethought from the ground up in terms of Intelligent Design."

Phillip Johnson, a lawyer who has been the central force in the Discovery Institute's promotion of ID, bemoans the secularization of American society and education. His primary example is Yale University, which, according to an 1898 history of Connecticut, was founded by clergy in 1701 from "a sincere regard to, and zeal for, upholding the Protestant religion, by a succession of learned and orthodox men." Johnson speaks dismissively of "the secular [E]nlightenment values of freedom of inquiry, political equality, and public service" that marked Yale's transition into the 20th century.

The ID movement is not a threat to the practice of science, but to the cultural and political atmosphere in which scientific research is conducted and children are educated. The attack on science is the cultural "canary in the coal mine." creationism, where it exists, is a symptom of a larger problem stemming not only from conservative disillusionment with the Enlightenment and the modern world but also from a deeply ingrained anti-intellectualism. Dembski and Johnson speak for a segment of the American public who cannot enunciate their intellectual and spiritual discomfort as well as Dembski and Johnson, but who can and do provide logistical support for their efforts. In its attempt during the last decade to undermine the teaching of evolution, the Discovery Institute has attacked the science teaching standards of several American States, with Texas being the most recent target (as of March 2009). Working with Religious Right groups, the ID movement has also coordinated the introduction of creationist legislation in eight States since 2008, with my State of Louisiana being, so far, the only State to adopt such legislation.

In recent years, creationists have tried to curtail the teaching of evolution in both the United Kingdom and continental Europe. In his final address as president of the Royal Society in 2005, Lord Robert May of Oxford expressed concern for the threat to the Enlightenment from "fundamentalist forces" that were "again on the march, West and East."

He specifically warned against the Discovery Institute's agenda. In 2006, the Royal Society issued a formal statement against teaching creationism. In October 2007, the Council of Europe adopted Resolution 1580, *The Dangers of creationism in Education*, warning that "if we are not careful, the values that are the very essence of the Council of Europe will be under direct threat from creationist fundamentalists. It is part of the role of the Council of Europe's parliamentarians to react before it is too late." This resolution followed the council's report citing creationist activity in Europe, including the rise of Muslim creationism, the Polish Deputy Minister of Education's branding evolutionary theory as a lie in 2006, the Italian Minister of Education's 2004 proposal to abolish the teaching of evolution in primary and secondary schools, the Dutch Minister of Education's 2005 endorsement of Intelligent Design, and numerous other examples. European opinion polls that show a higher than expected level of support for creationism bear out the Council of Europe's concern. Similar American polls over several decades have consistently reflected popular resistance to evolution. A February 2009 Gallup poll showed that only 39% of Americans accept evolution, with 25% not believing it, and 36% having no opinion either way. Polls in the United Kingdom are only marginally more encouraging. According to a 2008 ComRes poll commissioned by Theos, a public theology think tank, "around a quarter of the British population are committed in their adherence to Young Earth creationism or Intelligent Design, and at least as many again are uncertain in their attitude towards evolution, [which] translates into around 20 million adults who are more or less ill-disposed towards Darwinian evolution." Surveys in Germany and Italy have revealed increases in the number of people who, respectively, either reject evolution or want schools to teach both evolution and creationism. The European problem may stem not so much from creationism *per se* as from the general rise of religious fundamentalism. In America, creationism is a major problem in its own right, although it has benefited from the Religious Right's increasing political influence since the election of Ronald Reagan in 1980.

In both America and Europe, the problem has become sufficiently disturbing to prompt the staid *Financial Times* to issue a warning in January 2009:

"Many scientists and liberal politicians regard the rising creationist tide as a side-show that they can safely ignore. They are wrong, for several reasons. Wide areas of research, from biology to cosmology, would suffer directly if it became politically difficult for governments to fund fields that depend on such a basic a part of science as evolution. The cost would be economic as well as intellectual... We need far more scientists than are available today to speak out quickly and firmly when reason is under attack."

The *Financial Times*'s call for more public involvement by scientists echoes my own recommendation that scientists and academics in other fields, including the humanities, assume a higher civic profile in defense of science.

Kenneth Miller, a Brown University biologist and prominent ID critic, also calls upon scientists to respond. In his book, *Only a Theory: Evolution and the Battle for America's Soul,* he warns:

"The proponents of ID seek nothing less than a true scientific revolution, an uprising of the first order that would do a great deal more than just displace Darwin from our textbooks and curricula. They seek the undoing of four centuries of Western science, and that surely should be enough to make anyone sit up and pay attention."

American and European scientists are increasingly paying attention, but they are often unsure of what to do. During the Enlightenment, citizens became scientists. Now, in order to help restore the Enlightenment, scientists must embrace their role as citizens.

Combining support for science with personal civic engagement was integral to America's early governance. In his book *Science and the Founding Fathers*, I. Bernard Cohen wrote that "the Founding Fathers displayed a knowledge of scientific concepts and principles which establishes their credentials as citizens of the Age of Reason." Thomas Jefferson, Benjamin Franklin, John Adams, and James Madison, building on European science and political thought, epitomized the role of "citizen-scientist" that was vital to both science and religious freedom in colonial America. Jefferson served as president of America's first scientific organization, the American Philosophical Society. He wrote about his love of science and commitment to politics in response to a letter from Harry Innes, a fellow lawyer and science enthusiast: "Your first [letter] gives me information in the line of natural history and the second (not yet received) promises political news. The first is my passion, the last is my duty, and therefore both desireable." Franklin was a fellow of Britain's Royal Society and a member of the Académie Royale des Sciences in Paris. Adams founded the American Academy of Arts and Sciences and diligently studied science throughout his life. Under Jefferson's tutelage, Madison became a scientific devotee and amateur scientist.

Today a number of scientists have entered political life, among them Germany's Chancellor Angela Merkel, who has a PhD in physical chemistry. Nobel laureate Steven Chu is the new secretary of the US Department of Energy. Forty-seven members of the current US Congress have at least one math, science, or engineering degree, and the American Association for the Advancement of Science holds workshops to train scientists to run for political office. This is a worthy goal, even though, for most of us, it is unrealistic. Equally urgent is the task of creating a voice for science and Enlightenment values from within our respective civic infrastructures by becoming publicly engaged as ordinary citizens, and I emphasize the word "publicly." However, in America, and probably Europe to some extent, there are three major obstacles to such civic engagement: the widespread scientific illiteracy of our fellow citizens; the comfort of the ivory tower in which so many scientists and other academics work; aggressive political opposition from religious fundamentalists, and sometimes mainstream religious conservatives, both to science and to secular societal institutions. These obstacles raise the question of how the scientific community can address them.

The scientific illiteracy of the public is the most difficult obstacle in the short term. Scientific literacy requires long-term improvement in the way people are educated, which in turn requires improvement in teacher training and access to adequate schools for all children. Overcoming this obstacle depends to some extent on overcoming the second one, namely, the reluctance of scientists and other academics to become publicly engaged. Scientists can do much to address both obstacles simultaneously. For example, the European Molecular Biology Laboratory (EMBL) operates the European Learning Laboratory for the Life Sciences to provide research experiences for secondary school science teachers. The University of Lausanne operates L'Eprouvette, a scientific laboratory that invites the public to work with scientists in order to learn the nature of scientific research. The university also has a compulsory program in which biology students receive instruction and undertake projects concerning topics such as the ethical responsibilities of scientists for public well-being. In an article entitled "Teaching Scientists to Be Good Citizens," Prof. Jacques Dubochet of Lausanne's Department of Ecology and evolution stresses that "the time of the ivory tower is over" and that "scientists can no longer escape their role as citizens," despite the fact that "although being a scientist is a difficult job, being a good citizen is harder." However, Dubochet reassures his fellow scientists that "the big advantage of citizenship over biology is that it does not require broad factual knowledge; it mostly requires common sense." He adds that it also requires that scientists learn to communicate with the public, a point to which I would add that those with the best communication skills should put their expertise at the service of teachers and students in elementary and secondary schools. In addition, scientists must actively cultivate a relationship with print and broadcast media and be willing to use it.

There are other specific measures that scientists can take. Well-known scientists such as Kenneth Miller in America and Richard Dawkins in England embrace their roles as public defenders of science. Less well-known scientists are active in "citizens for science" groups, which exist in roughly a dozen American States. They work against creationist legislation and help fend off creationist attacks on State science-teaching standards. Some campaign for pro-science political candidates, while some run for office themselves on local and State boards of education. Some who are people of faith serve as pro-science liaisons to their religious communities. In a broad movement called Science Debate 2008, American scientists and concerned citizens worked together during the recent presidential campaign to urge candidates to address scientific issues. This group can arguably claim much of the credit for Obama's public reassurance to the pro-science community in his inaugural address.

This kind of civic engagement is vital in a democracy to cultivating a public constituency for science and Enlightenment values. However, such efforts are easy compared to the challenge presented by the third obstacle, religious fundamentalism. In Western democracies, the worst excesses of religious opposition to science and the teaching of evolution have so far been preventable in the short term because most citizens reject the fundamentalist agenda. American federal courts have traditionally ruled in favor of the separation of Church and State, and such rulings benefit both science and education. creationists have so far been defeated consistently in American courts. But that line of defense is now less certain because of George Bush's appointment of a number of conservative ideologues to lifetime positions as federal judges. If European creationists are anything like American ones, their most consistent characteristic is their persistent refusal to go away, and they always find accommodating politicians.

The factor that ultimately makes counteracting religious fundamentalism so difficult is the problem of epistemology. In its Resolution 1580, the Council of Europe rightly urged Member States to "strengthen the teaching of the foundations of science, its history, and its epistemology and its methods." This is politically vital, although explaining epistemology to the public presents a distinct challenge. Whereas science and other empirical disciplines have both a successful methodology and an epistemology for expanding our cumulative knowledge of nature and society, super-naturalist religions have neither; consequently, their adherents can offer no base of common religious knowledge on which to ground public policy. This is the most fundamental reason for the epistemological impasse between science and super-naturalist religion, and specifically between evolution and creationism. Nonetheless, with the support of self-serving politicians, creationists are trying to craft public policy so as to give their personal religious commitments the force of law. In America they recently succeeded when Louisiana Gov. Bobby Jindal signed the deceptively named 2008 Louisiana Science Education Act, allowing science teachers in government schools to use creationist teaching materials. Jindal is allied with the Louisiana Family Forum, a Religious Right group that is part of a national network and that works closely with the Discovery Institute.

Public policy in a democracy must be grounded in common knowledge, an issue requiring a fuller discussion than I can include here. However, if explaining evolution to a scientifically illiterate public is a daunting task, explaining the epistemological problem concerning science and super-naturalist religion will likely be more so. While acknowledging that "not all faith is incompatible with science and secular reason" (such as, for example, pantheism and some branches of Buddhism), biologist Jerry Coyne enunciates this epistemological problem succinctly:

> *"It would appear, then, that one cannot be coherently religious and scientific at the same time. That alleged synthesis requires that with one part of your brain you accept only those things that are tested and supported by agreed-upon evidence, logic, and reason, while with the other part of your brain you accept things that*

are unsupportable or even falsified. In other words, the price of philosophical harmony is cognitive dissonance. Accepting both science and conventional faith leaves you with a double standard: rational on the origin of blood clotting, irrational on the Resurrection; rational on dinosaurs, irrational on virgin births... So the most important conflict is not between religion and science. It is between religion and secular reason. Secular reason includes science, but also embraces moral and political philosophy, mathematics, logic, history, journalism, and social science - every area that requires us to have good reasons for what we believe."

This is a crucial message to convey to politicians, and there is at least one American politician who understands this epistemological problem.

In *The Audacity of Hope*, Barack Obama reveals his understanding of the gulf between science and religion that must be bridged by civic friendship and compromise since it cannot be bridged epistemically:

"For those who believe in the inerrancy of the Bible, as many evangelicals do, such rules of engagement may seem just one more example of the tyranny of the secular and material worlds over the sacred and eternal. But in a pluralistic democracy, we have no choice. Almost by definition, faith and reason operate in different domains and involve different paths to discerning truth. Reason - and science - involves the accumulation of knowledge based on realities that we can all apprehend. Religion, by contrast, is based on truths not provable through ordinary human understanding - the belief in things not seen. When science teachers insist on keeping creationism or Intelligent Design out of their classrooms, they are not asserting that scientific knowledge is superior to religious insight [but] simply that each path to knowledge involves different rules and that those rules are not interchangeable politics, like science, depends on our ability to persuade each other of common aims based on a common reality. Moreover, politics (unlike science) involves compromise, the art of the possible. At some fundamental level, religion does not allow for compromise. It insists on the impossible. If God has spoken, then followers are expected to live up to God's edicts, regardless of the consequences. To base one's life on such uncompromising commitments may be sublime; to base our policy making on such commitments would be a dangerous thing. So the best we can do is act in accordance with those things that are possible for all of us to know."

The problem of creationism has no quick and easy solution. In the short term, there must be constitutional constraints against the civic and educational damage that religious fundamentalists and their politician-accomplices can do. Coupled with these constraints, however, must be the acceptance by scientists and other academics of the civic responsibility of helping to restore the legacy of the Enlightenment.

*Department of History & Political Science,
Southeastern Louisiana University, USA

Amedeo Santosuosso*
**May scientific research work as a model
for present transnational law?**

Let me offer my sincere thanks to the organizers, and particularly
to Marco Cappato, for this invitation. As with John Harris, this is also
my second opportunity to speak at the World Congress for Freedom
of Scientific Research, and I feel very honoured for that.

In choosing a subject to discuss with you this evening, the initial
temptation was to choose something fresh, not to repeat the arguments in favour of constitutional protection for scientific research
which I discussed on the first occasion, and to say that the time had
come to stop complaining about the restrictions to which freedom
of scientific research is subjected. This led me to decide instead to
speak about the positive role science plays as a model of social action and an example of cultural activity subject to continuous rigorous inspection by peers, as well as by society and its institutions. But
I then thought that it would be necessary, however swiftly, to reiter-
ate a few points, still relevant, regarding the protection of the freedom of scientific research from the point of view of constitutional
law.

I should first of all state that if we are speaking of science and the
law, we are using terms which are very comprehensive, and hence
rather vague. Naturally, among the various cases and interaction
modes existing between them, there are some, where the impact of
science on the law is dominant, while in others it is the other way
round. The aspect which I should like to take as a starting point, albeit briefly, is the impact of the law, or in a wider sense, of the legal
environment, on scientific research. The first point, then, is as follows: is freedom to carry out scientific research protected by the constitution? Whenever I visit the laboratory of one of those scientists
who put up with my invasions and those of my students, the first
thing I tell them is that they should not forget that their activity is
"under constitutional protection"! I think it is fair to state that this is
the rule throughout the developed world, and that the restrictions
(which are indeed possible in the presence of a level of law which
takes precedence) constitute an exception which must be strictly

justified, and not merely a possible moral option on the part of a government, an institution, an organised religion or a party.

At times, indeed, you get the impression that scientists were among the first to internalise a form of distrust which arises from certain religious environments. Sometimes, in fact, the distrust comes from political and cultural positions which, while not explicitly inspired by religion, do, however, place scientific knowledge at the same level (with its temporary nature, which is part of it) as social and religious beliefs (being incapable of verification, also in their nature) and so produce a kind of devaluation of what science can give: verified knowledge which offers itself for further verification and also refutation.

One of the crucial problems is that of human dignity. In Europe we have the Charter of basic human rights for the citizens of Europe (otherwise known as the Charter of Nice) which, in article 13 states that the arts and scientific research must be free of any restrictions. A reading of the official explanation of this article shows that freedom of scientific research is based on and derives from the right of freedom of expression and thought, seen throughout the world as the basis of democratic systems. We also learn, moreover, that this must be exercised with regard to article 1 of the same Charter, which affirms the inviolability of human dignity. This actually gives rise to a delicate problem regarding the relationship between human dignity and freedom of scientific research. If, as some people seem to accept, human dignity is allowed to take precedence over scientific research, this creates a situation in which whoever holds, or claims, the power to define human dignity in all matters also holds the power to limit or nullify individual freedom, including the freedom to carry out scientific research. For my part, however, I stand with those for whom dignity which is in contrast with freedom is impossible, and that a man or woman whose freedom has been restricted on the basis of a notion of dignity defined by others would on those grounds alone be deprived of their dignity. It is therefore the limitation to freedom which require justification, not freedom itself.

Another example, different but significant, of how reasoning of a moral nature can have an important effect on rights and freedoms arises from the recent decision by the Enlarged Board of Appeal of the European Patent Office, which has excluded the patentability of embryonic stem cells of human origin, the reasoning being based on its being contrary to public order and good custom (decision G 2/06, the WARF case, November 25, 2008). Of course, you can think all the evil you wish about intellectual property rights, that they are a bad thing, that they are a way of privately appropriating public knowledge or the like, but the reasoning on which the European Patent Office denied the patentability of stem cells in this case in question is such that it is not even likely to please the enemies of the intellectual property system. The rejection is in fact based on a broad and radical interpretation of the limits of a moral nature which Community standards impose. In summary, and without getting into technicalities, it could be claimed that the judges refused to make any distinction and adopted a strict position (morally, not from the point of view of logic or science) according to which from the moment the stem cells are of human derivation, they are by definition not patentable since they contravene public order and morality. Why this is serious in my opinion is because when they set that limit, they made no distinctions about the conditions governing the embryo from which those cells were processed (whether it was an abandoned embryo, an embryo with biological malformations which would render it anyway unsuitable to develop into a foetus or in other conditions which deprived it of the potential to become a developed human being, which is the foundation for the strictest positions on the subject). Rather the discussion was in general and indiscriminate terms.

Having said this, I should like to propose what in my opinion is a short list of what are the essential aspects of the constitutional protection of freedom to carry out scientific research. In the first place, it is a good thing that the law actually does not intervene to regulate scientific research and the means adopted for the process, especially if the matter in hand is concerned with research largely unconnected with extensive technological applications. This is the best option, on the assumption that the funding for the research comes from the public coffers, as is indeed required by many European constitutions, including that of Italy. In the second place, it is possible that there may arise a requirement to regulate the research in order to prevent possible breaches of the rights of third parties, or individuals, who may be harmed by the research itself. In this case the protections and restrictions are justified, but must be adopted only to the extent they are strictly necessary. In the third place, it is necessary for the law to avoid acting like a secular arm of some religion or a particular worldview. The division between the law and morality (and hence any religious belief) is the basis of modern liberty: we must not allow ourselves to abandon this fundamental point. Well, I am very sorry to have to say it, but Italy meets none of these requirements. This leads me to my fourth point, which would be to look to other countries: do not follow Italy's example.

Moving on to the central argument of my contribution, I would like to take as my basis the notion that it is not only the law which has an effect on science - the opposite is also true, that science affects the law in a variety of ways. One of these, for example, is the construction of the notion of natural according to scientific parameters and the influence which this has on the conceptual objectives which we consider as natural within the disciplinary ambit of the law. In legal reasoning, both theoretical and in current practice, there exists a series of conceptual and cultural assumptions which are taken as read and which are not re-examined every day or in response to changes in detail. These could be seen as natural from the legal point of view, at least in the sense that they endow the assumptions with a degree of stability (albeit wholly relative), in counterposition to the clearly artificial nature of the law in the way it produces detail, be that in respect of legislation or precedent (it is hard to see a legislative decree on milk quotas or the like as not artificial). It turns out that science and the conflicts which the application of science generates have an impact on the nature-related assumptions (not discussed) of the law, which appear in their nature as artificial, even if deployed for a longer period of time.

In my opinion, there are two main points of the impact of science on the law today: the individual as a physical individual and of the nation State. Here I shall swiftly develop a few thoughts about the second point. According to an idea received from twentieth-century tradition, the order of the State ought to be a closed, self-sufficient structure, lacking in communications, albeit not at the level of, or across, the highest levels of States. This idea was initially thrown into question by the information technology revolution and the movement of information this made possible. Legal professionals and lawyers were accustomed to work within national, closed frameworks, while nowadays, thank to the computers on their desks, they can access legal case law, legislation and theory from other countries. The language barrier does exist, but access to this type of information is now a well-established reality within the reach of all. In the second place, legal professionals and judges found that they had to handle conflicts connected with scientific applications, particularly of a biological nature. However, apart from their high level of social relevance, these conflicts are scarcely of national importance. If we wonder whether DNA is the property of the individual, while admitting that the legal definition of property varies from country to country, we must recognise that the basic problem - that of regarding DNA as property or not - is raised throughout the world in the same way, at least as far as its biological characteristics are concerned, from the moment when the scientific applications have the same characteristics. The outcome has been that within the legal world an attitude has developed which favours looking outside of one's own country, to assess the sources and precedents of other countries. There is resistance to this, mainly of a linguistic, but also cultural and political nature. For example, in the United States for some years a genuinely fierce debate has raged as to the possibility of quoting foreign sources. Nowadays, however, it can be said that the trend towards observing foreign experiences has been confirmed, and this is also a consequence of the impact of science on the law (as well as the growth of economic transactions at the global level).

There were two fundamental focal points in this process. In the 1990s it was realised that legal developments in a variety of countries were in reality very similar to what had been expected. This coincidence, at first unrecognized, whereby very often the judges in different countries ruled in the same way, while knowing nothing of the respective decisions, became, in the '90s, a recognized coincidence and in many cases was investigated. What is new in recent years is the general acceptance that this happens. While not everyone is in agreement, the fact that the courts of one country are referring to the legislation or precedents of other countries, now has the force of evidence. The recognition that the work of the legal professional is changing is still in the process of development, as is the knowledge that it is now essential to learn to be a lawyer in a different way, even though it is not completely clear how.

The current situation presents a somewhat chaotic appearance, where the old standards which presided over the social regulation system are being lost, or it may be that they are simply being added to by others, partly in conflict. One of the questions being asked is into which discipline fields can these situations be incorporated and whether it is possible to envisage the establishment of a consistent body of principles for the new production of legislation at transnational level. In these chaotic situations affecting the law in general, it is science which is appearing, raising the question as to what role it can play in the development of a fresh body of basic concepts. Can science, one of the most powerful players in this legal earthquake, be both a solution and an aid to the discovery of possible solutions?

The English-speaking countries have a well-known tradition of comparing science and the law. I should like to quote one writer here, Jeremy Waldron, who, in an article in the *Harvard Law Review* of 2005, made a very neat, you might even say simplistic, suggestion. He maintained that the law had to learn to "behave like science". Science has never claimed to be infallible and at the global level constitutes a huge store available for the researcher who wants to carry out research. In the same way, claims Waldron, "the law of nations", an expression by which the author means the totality of the law as it develops at world level, is at the disposal of legislators and judges from all countries, as are all the rules, principles and decisions used to settle the cases. Waldron then states, apparently in provocative and naïve terms, that just as science does not claim to be infallible, the *ius gentium* should not claim to be the whole truth. What is important is for these solutions to work in the settlement of the case.

A number of objections can be made to this suggestion. In the first place it sets judges and national parliaments on the same level, which is not by any means the case, not even in the provisions of common law. It throws into confusion any notion of a hierarchy of the sources of law, in that it admits that a judge can refer to precedent from one country or another (only in respect of the ability of the precedent to settle the case), and hence it would be difficult to find a criterion of legitimacy which would justify that choice; nor is it clear how the peer review system could be applied in the transnational legal field, which, because it is always under discussion, remains one of the guarantees of quality existing in the scientific field. Despite this, the proposal has some interesting aspects. First and foremost, it is clearly stated that Waldron's proposal does not bring about the destruction of anything which had not already been destroyed or was at least in a serious state of crisis. In the second place, it spotlights the way in which the courts, while referring to precedents in other countries, are *de facto* adhering to a criterion of quality, of functionality, which is completely different from the traditional, and typically juridical, criterion of legitimation. And then, is it presently possible to contain within national boundaries legal reason relating to questions such as those connected with science? Judges are beginning to reason from a tiny, but important, point of view. When each of us decides a case or formulates a theory, we know that this is not only subject to the scrutiny of the national community of our own country, but is being observed by the international community. This represents a huge difference in the culture of legal professionals and is an indication that a global community of legal professionals is being created.

Waldron's thesis is too simple and is successful only in that it has shaken up a kind of intellectual torpor, but we must press forward. I believe that we should regard science not as a model or a recipe to follow, but as a travelling companion with which we can become involved in a profitable dialogue from which we can draw suggestions and ideas. The first thing to be done as far as I can see, and above all in the area of science and the law, is to adopt a kind of experimental approach - to collect legislative or legal material from any country, to organize it in a system which has a degree of consistency, to note the relationships which appear between them, to set up links between the individuals in the various countries, who are concerned with the same argument, and to see if any consistent frameworks emerge in what an intelligence focused on the past would see as chaos.

This is the basic philosophy behind a project launched at the University of Pavia. Every legal case, every legislative source is presented as a kind of elementary particle, which has relationships with other elementary particles, in one's own or other countries, or in other contexts. Seen from this point of view, the model of the law which is becoming apparent, and which we observe, is not so far from the models present in the scientific area. This means that now, for the first time in many centuries, there is a real possibility of an advantageous reciprocal cross-fertilisation between law and science, of enormous mutual benefit. This is only possible, however, if the law, and its interpreters, and science, are free, because if this fundamental is missing, then everything rapidly collapses.

*Judge, Milan Court of Appeal, Italy

The challenges for reproductive medicine in Europe
Session proposed by
ESHRE - European Society of Human Reproduction

Anna Veiga*
Reproductive medicine and stem cells

I also wanted to thank the European Parliament and all of you for being here. It is a good opportunity for the ESHRE - European Society for Human Reproduction and Embryology to participate in this session. The topic of my presentation is reproductive medicine and stem cells. This last summer, it was 30 years from the birth of the first IVF - in vitro fertilisation - baby, in the United Kingdom. And this field in fact opened the way to the field of embryonic stem cells research.

The development of human embryos in the laboratory to get pregnancies paved the way to be able to derive embryonic stem cells and to obtain and use them in the lab for research. The first publication on embryonic stem cells, through the use of donated embryos, was published in 1998. The number of publications in this field has been increasing. hESC - human embryonic stem cells - come from the inner cell mass of human embryos at day 5-7 of development. They have between 150 and 200 cells. These cells, when in appropriate culture conditions, can give rise to all differentiated cells of the adult body (ectoderm, mesoderm and endoderm). The main characteristics of these embryonic stem cells are self-renewal and potentiality or the possibility of differentiation. These are called pluripotent cells. Many different cells have been obtained through differentiation in the mouse and human species. Research in this field paves the way to try to obtain an effective cell therapy.

Nuclear reprogramming is a technique that involves two different techniques. One is Somatic Cell Nuclear Transfer that has provided results in animal models but not in the human. The reprogramming of the nucleus is performed in this case through the oocyte. There is a need for oocyte donors for research if we want to develop this technique. This is a major problem. An alternative to the reprogramming of somatic cells has been found, i.e. the use of inter-species nuclear transfer by using bovine oocytes. The results so far with this technique are not very promising with regards to efficiency.

The other technique is the obtention of IPS - induced pluripotent stem cells through cell-reprogramming. This scientific breakthrough has come since Yamanaka published the first on the possibility to reprogram cells. This is done by the injection and transfer of certain genes, related to pluripotency. The cells obtained are in fact quite similar to hESC. They share the potentiality of self-renewal and differentiation. They are different combinations of genes that can be used to promote this inducement of pluripotent stem cells. The final goal of this technique would be to try to obtain specific IPS cells from specific patients to have models of disease in the lab and to be able to try to put in place cell therapy while studying the mechanisms of disease and the effect of drugs.

I only wanted to mention two other types of stem cells related to the field of reproductive medicine: endometrial and myometrial stem cells. These cells have proven to be multipotent. Endometrial stem cells can be isolated from menstrual blood and have shown to be involved in diseases, such as endometriosis. With regard to myometrial stem cells, it has been shown that they are involved in pathologies related to myoma. Another source of stem cells related to reproduction are amniotic fluid stem cells. These have been found in amniotic fluid that has been used in prenatal diagnosis. They are able to be maintained in an undifferentiated state and to differentiate in multiple cell types.

Let me say something briefly about cell therapy. As you can see in this journal, this is in the media more and more often. It involves the use of the cells of different origins, including embryonic, fetal and adult stem cells. A number of diseases can be considered as possible candidates for stem cell therapy, such as spinal cord, diabetes, cardiovascular disease, etc. One important thing to note is that embryonic stem cells have not yet been used for treatment for cell therapy. The first multicentre trial is now being put in place. It has been approved in 2009. They pretend to treat patients with spinal cord injury with embryonic stem cells differentiated to neural precursors. As an end, I wanted to tell you that we are coordinating an European project, funded by the European Commission, the human embryonic stem cell registry. In this website we have put in place all the information regarding more than 600 embryonic stem cell lines. Also pluripotent Ips cells have been included in this registry. It is a tool for scientists, regulators and the public to facilitate the finding of the cells that each research centre or lab is intended to use. It also shows the situation with regard to the legislation on embryonic stem cells and research in Europe and the world.

*Spain

Lone Schmidt*
Reproduction and the population crisis

(Prof. Schmidt kindly asked not to publish the transcription of her intervention. The slides of her presentation are available on the website of the World Congress: www.freedomofresearch.org/?q=Schmidt)

*Denmark

Joep Geraedts*
Genetics and reproductive health

I would like to talk about genetics and reproductive health, which means that I want to talk about two sides of the same coin that are strongly connected in several ways.

I would like to discuss three aspects today, though there are many more: firstly, I will talk about the genetic diagnosis of infertility; then, I will discuss genetic methods to improve the quality of assisted reproduction; finally, I will talk about the use of assisted reproduction to give more options to people with genetic problems, quoting some examples. I will be unable to talk about all aspects of the topic, for obvious reasons.

Let me begin with the genetic causes among women: as you may have heard, older women find increasingly more problematic getting pregnant, which is often related to chromosome abnormalities; these are not genetic as such, rather they are related to ageing.

There are many diseases in which genetic abnormalities cause infertility, and more research is needed on this. One example relates to premature ovarian failure, which hits one in a hundred women before the age of forty: there you will find a number of chromosome and genome abnormalities. However, even in a group of women where 90% of abnormalities are non-genetic, the remaining 10% may still be genetic: for example, with endometriosis, which is frequent among women, there is a genetic component but it is hard to detail it. In spite of the many studies being carried out, the location of the different genes involved in this disease is yet unknown, although the chromosomes indicate that there may be a genetic cause. This disease serves as an example of one which affects quite a number of women and where genetics are involved.

There are as many chromosome abnormalities in males as in females, numerical as well as structural, particularly in the Y chromosome where defects are found with increasing frequency.

There are all sorts of genetic abnormalities to be found in animals used for experiments, where thousands of genes involved in reproduction can be mutated; similarly, there may be many more abnormalities yet to be found in the future with regard to the human species. This concludes our short introduction on genetic diagnosis of infertility.

Let us now move on to treatments, which start by bringing together male and female gametes: normally, half the chromosomes from the gametes of both parents are sufficient, and then the full number is restored after fertilisation, which means that 23 from each side should give 46 - a new individual. Studying these chromosomes in some detail, with the split between 23 paternal and maternal ones, shows that sometimes the reduction to half is abnormal, which often happens with older women, and where the oocyte may show 24 chromosomes, leading to a total of 47 chromosomes after fertilisation and an abnormal embryo. This type of chromosome abnormality, mostly noticed after birth, is Down syndrome, in which there are three copies of chromosome 21 instead of two. However, other numerical chromosome abnormalities can also be seen, and most of these are not observed at birth because they start during fertilisation and fail during pregnancy because they are not viable.

Avoiding such abnormalities during IVF embryo transfer helps avoid problems after implantation or during pregnancy: many years ago it seemed reasonable to study chromosomes to see if they were normal and then transfer only the embryos with normal chromosomes, which led to the procedure known as FISH (fluorescence in situ hybridization), where one of the cells from the embryo is placed on a slide and stained with a particular method that allows to look at the chromosomes. This can now be done routinely for most but not all chromosomes, which allows to spot abnormalities: what this allows us to do is to use PGS (pre-implantation genetic screening) to select those embryos that have the correct number of chromosomes, which leads to better chances of a normal pregnancy.

It looks as though all cells have the same genetic material, which means that if you take out one cell to study the embryo you can then predict the chromosome number of all other cells, for example, if you observe a green cell, you can predict that all other cells are also green. However, since 1994 we have been aware of a problem known as mosaicism: for example, given an embryo of eight cells, you might find that not all cells are similar, so that a green or red cell would not represent the whole embryo. This may lead to mistakes such as taking out a normal embryo, or transferring an abnormal one. Unfortunately this means that the current methods are not working, and that we should look at the oocyte before it is fertilised, since that is where the majority of real abnormalities are present, so bypassing mosaicism. Consequently, we have started a project at ESHRE where we study the oocyte by means of its counterpart, the polar body, which in itself presents the problem of a screening where you may not be able to look at all the chromosomes at the same time. We hope therefore to introduce a new method that would allow us to look at all the chromosomes at the same time, which is preferable.

Where assisted reproduction is available, it may be used also on people with genetic abnormalities through PGD (pre-implantation genetic diagnosis) - a combination of IVF and genetic testing – to avoid transmission from one generation to the next of genetic diseases as a whole, rather than just of oocyte or embryo abnormalities. So if one of the parents has a genetic abnormality there may be no alternative than PGD, for other alternatives may be either unavailable or impractical and may leave the couple with a 50% risk of having an abnormal child. You may even have to refrain from having children, as adoption is not always an option. Also, egg/sperm donation is difficult in many countries, and prenatal diagnosis is also problematic – although widely accepted due to the lack of alternatives. Now, however, we do have the option of PGD, which is better than prenatal diagnosis where you examine a fetus that is already 12-16 weeks old and decide from there whether it is normal or abnormal - and perhaps decide to terminate the pregnancy. This is not easy to do and some people would prefer a method that occurred much earlier in the process, which is the case with PGD as it is done at the eight-cell stage and only requires one or two cells (normally just one) with results available within 24 hours. So, if you only need one cell and one day, the method becomes crucial and correct in nearly 100% of the cases.

The problem with many diseases is the variety of methods available, each starting with the selection of a cell for lab analysis, also known as a biopsy, where many aspects can be examined, including sex determination (for sex-linked diseases such as Duchenne or haemophilia), chromosome abnormalities (especially structural ones), or gene mutations. Humans have 25,000 different genes, leading to a variety of diseases, and we can analyse about two hundred at the moment, with the possibility of applying HLA (human leukocyte antigen) typing – post-natal stem cell transplantation from cord blood. The top ten monogenic diseases we have studied during the last ten years remain relatively constant, and as I have said in the introduction we have collected data on this at ESHRE through the ESHRE PGD Consortium. Research and development will allow many more diseases to be diagnosed in the future, although this may take years. Often it is not only a case of having monogenic diseases but of being susceptible to developing them, which means that more research is needed to know all the factors involved. I already mentioned new emergent strategies for single-cell genetic analysis where one may have an overview and allow for more and more techniques to be developed and applied at single-cell stage. We are very optimistic and hopeful about identifying many diseases through this method.

I believe that the future depends on technological advances but also on regulation, and I hope we may see more being done by politicians in this area at European and at national level in particular.

We hope that there will be less fragmentation within European politics, in parallel with that concerning embryo research - there are many EU countries where PGD is allowed, and a minority where it is not. Fragmentation within the EU allows such diversity, and some countries have no legislation with regard to PGD - where the latter is allowed, it may be so under a number of limiting caveats, which would be too long to detail here.

The variables of the disorder that are most important in this respect are age of onset, penetrance and severity. Chances of prevention or treatment for the latter are significant. The ultimate question is: where can we draw the line? Many may say that it was acceptable if you had monogenic conditions - which will manifest themselves. What about conditions with incomplete penetrance and/or variable expression, which are sometimes severe and sometimes mild? And what about risk factors for medical conditions, undesirable traits and non-disease traits? If you look at the literature you will see that different lines are drawn.

Finally I wish to mention that there has been a document on this topic issued in 2006 by the European Society of Human Genetics, the ESHRE and the PGD Consortium. I wish to thank all my colleagues who were involved with preparing this document, which you will find in the literature.

* ESHRE Chairman,
The Netherlands

Luca Gianaroli*

Assisted reproduction in Europe

One of the tasks of ESHRE, as it has already been said, is to monitor the results and activities around Europe. This is done via our consortium. Every year we publish our report on human reproduction.

This report covers a large majority of the activities done in Europe. It has to deal with the quantity and availability of the data, the figures, the quality, the risks and the trends. I will try to go through these five points briefly.

First of all we have countries around Europe in which they already have national registries. There are 16 listed. We also have countries in which data are collected directly by us because they do not have national registries. We can have all the data from all the clinics from Belgium to Croatia, Denmark, UK etc. Moreover we have a proportion of clinics that report to us from 16 countries. There are countries in which at least 10,000 treatments are done every year: France, Germany, UK, Italy etc. So we are talking about roughly 400,000 or half a million treatments registered every year. It is a quite a large database. Some conclusions can be drawn.

First of all, you know that we have two major techniques. One is IVF (in vitro fertilisation) the other one is ICSI (intracytoplasmic sperm injection). From 1997 - when we started to register - to 2005, there has been a change in technology. The most sophisticated technologies are used more. We have reached a point in which two out of three treatments are done through ICSI technologies, while only one out of three is done through IVF. If you split these data according to the countries, you see that there are huge differences.

Take for instance the Italian situation. My choice is due to the fact that in this country we have a strict regulation. As you can see, if you compare Europe with Italy, despite patients having the same problems and the same pathologies, when you have very strict regulation, more sophisticated and expensive techniques are used with the aim to help overcoming the lower success rate. So, this is just an example of how techniques sometimes are not driven by clinical indication or medical decision-making, but by legislation and local rules put in place.

Availability means a number of circles for one million inhabitants. There are countries in Europe where these techniques are used very well, so, they are available in large numbers. But then you see in some countries, where for instance reimbursement is not completely available, the possibility to have access to this technology drops very low. One example are the UK and Switzerland where you can see that the number of cycles is very low for one million of inhabitants. If you look at another country like Italy, with 6 million people, the availability of these techniques is very low compared to the other countries. We do not have the 2006 data for the other countries, yet, but this is the trend that we are looking for. It is also interesting to note that if you look at the total amount of babies born, due to these techniques, compared to the whole population, there are countries like Denmark in which one baby out of 30 is now born thanks to this technology. This amount decreases in some countries and it is reduced to 1/3, such as in Switzerland and UK. This diversity is quite again well expressed when you compare countries with very strict regulation. For instance in Italy you have a 1 out of 100 compared to 3,5 out of 100 in Denmark. Moreover the availability of these techniques sometimes is not related to the quality of the healthcare system but it is due to the reimbursement policies or to the local law policies.

Let's consider the efficacy and the trends now, also referring to the percentage of pregnancies per transferred embryos. The European data clearly show an increasing trend. In ten years, the trends of these techniques are getting safer and more successful, little by little through a lot of activities and research. If you compare once more Europe with a country where a restrictive law has been only recently adopted, you see a discrepancy between Europe and the countries that followed the European trend before. Now there is a dichotomy between the increase of success rate of Europe and the increase of success rate of patients' treatments in Italy in this case. It does not matter if you use ICSI or IVF. Even if you keep the same standard, clinics, environments, doctors, same patients, you have a dramatic decrease in terms of costs and treatments and the need for the patients to enter again the same treatment, to overcome the limitation of their country.

I would like to say a few words on quality and trends. As for quality, it has already been mentioned, implanting less possible embryos is aimed at reducing the risk of multiple pregnancies. There are countries where three or more embryos are transferred and this of course plays a role in terms of risk of multiple pregnancies.

Take once more for instance Italy where in 2005-2006 there was no decrease on the tendency to transfer many embryos, because clinicians were forced by law to transfer them all in Italy, because conservation of embryos was not allowed in that country. It means that you have countries like Albania, Serbia and Italy, in which the risk of delivery with complication of triplets is very high. It goes from 5,7 to 2,7. Then there are what we call the safe countries in which the technique is correctly applied. They dramatically decrease from 2,7 pregnancies in Italy to 0,4 or 0,2 in countries like Finland, that is ten times less risk of having complication by multiple pregnancies.

As for safety and risk, one of the risks that I would like to mention here is the possibility that some countries in Europe really apply these technologies in such a way, that they dramatically differ from other countries. We have compared the number of ART (assisted reproduction techniques) cycles for one million of inhabitants with the gross domestic product (GDP) in some of these countries. There are countries which perform very well in terms of production of treatments if compared with the gross domestic product. Some of them, however, do not. There is a big group of European countries, including Switzerland and Italy, where the GDP is high, but the number of treatments is still very low. By example consider Germany.

Finally, take the amount of money invested in ART cycles per million of inhabitants and the amount of money spent in social security compared with the GDP. These percentages go from 10 to 22%. These countries are scattered, e.g. Italy, UK and Switzerland are considered as healthy countries, but they are still investing very little in this field.

We can consider two other parameters to conclude. We can compare these countries referring to the technology index, the technological readiness of research, development, creativity then you see how the countries are scattered. This shows a huge difference among the European countries. I would like to conclude by saying that one of the things that ESHRE is doing is to closely monitor reproductive tourism. A paper on this huge problem - since it implies movement of population from one country to another according to the different local law - has been recently produced by the International Federation of Fertility Society. Patients mobility around Europe for medical problems has always been considered as a positive thing because it has been evaluated as a patient right to have access to high-level healthcare but referring to reproduction you are negatively impressed by the image of patients looking for something strange or trivial. This is a huge problem ESHRE is going to address through a special task force that will take care of this. We hope the data will be soon available.

*ESHRE Chairman elect, Italy

Paul de Vroey*
Healthy babies and safe treatments

When we treat people for infertility one of the most important points is the health of women and children. Many issues are related to it. One of them is: are these treatments safe and do we have the tools in our hands to do them safely? In fact we are on a daily basis our own enemies, that is:

• we stimulate the ovaries;

• we get multiple pregnancies at any time a new technique is introduced;

• (we can influence the) birth rate.

It has been said before: we have to be careful when we make laws to make techniques safe for the children. In the United States, more of half of the children born through these techniques are multiple pregnancies. In Europe there is a strange situation: especially in those countries where the law takes care of the multiple pregnancies there is a huge difference. There is absolutely no reason to implant more embryos. We looked at a paper by Donoso: even after PGD (pre-implantation genetic diagnosis), sometimes one or two embryos are implanted. There is no reason to be forced by law to implant many embryos. The question is: how can we improve the results? For instance we can implant at day three or day five. In fact we published in the *Journal of Medicine* that the delivery rate is significantly higher at day five, 37% versus 24% during this particular one-embryo implantation strategy.

We have been extremely concerned with the health of the children. In 2002 we dedicated a paper to it. The prematurity rate is significantly different between twins and singletons. Women think, that twins are not a problem, but twins are a huge problem and we have to be aware of this situation. Look at weight at birth. It is extremely different between singletons and twins. For instance 3,000 grams for singletons and 2,000 for twins. Admission to neonatal units is a difference, with a 60% of the twins having had to go to neonatal units. Also think about the triplets as mentioned by Dr. Gianaroli. We have to understand that the low birth weight is associated with increased adult diseases. It is incomprehensible that you are forced to implant more than one embryo.

It is safer for children when we introduce a technique in our department; we are concerned with the safety and health of the children. The chromosomal abnormalities have slightly increased, especially because when you take sperm of the husband, you have to take care of the health of the husband, as pointed out by Prof. Geraedts.

In 2002 we compared the malformation rates in babies born after ICSI (intracytoplasmic sperm injection) and IVF (in vitro fertilisation). For the singletons, it is 3% by ICSI and 3% by IVF. Very similar data, and the same is true for twins and triplets. That is reassuring.

We looked at the malformation rates. There is a paper from Ludwig, Germany, a very recent paper of 2009. According to the ICSI group and control group, the malformation rates, also the minor ones, are exactly the same, about 10% by ICSI and IVF. This is reassuring for the health of the newborns. So, singleton children born after IVF, compared to spontaneous, still have a problem, what is related to the fact that these women are infertile. If you think of how to make it safe, we need a lot more research and other laws in different European countries, by focusing on avoiding multiple pregnancies and hyperstimulation syndrome. Look at the data of 2006. About 1% had hyperstimulation syndrome. We need research to avoid it. We can avoid it if we use different drug system, with antagonist and agonist.

There is a beautiful paper published recently explaining that there are high pregnancy rates in America. That is research is progressing and helping infertile women. There was also a paper from Luca's group of 1999, stating that where there is any risk for hyperstimulation syndrome, you can freeze the extra embryos.

In the same line of research, with data from Germany, there are new systems of vitrification, whereby you can improve the results. There is a paper of 2006, explaining that embryos were frozen, by trying to improve the system. This is extremely important: if you look at a randomized trial by Catt, you see that the results between low freezing, classical one and vitrification, gives 18 versus 36% improvement. That is highly significant. Research is mandatory and progressing. Consider the data published in Japan in 2008, with a malformation rate of 3% - remember the data after ICSI, IVF and conception: they are always about 3% - on a quite important cohort of children (700).

My conclusion is that there are two elements in this field:
• the laws have to change in those countries where you are forced

to do bad practice;

• our research has to change to make it very simple and safer for women. All these data confirm it, together with all the new drugs available and all the vitrification systems we have.

*Belgium

(Extra-sessional speeches)

Audrey Simpson*
**The legal, political and social context
of the provision of abortion services in Northern Ireland**

I want to highlight how women in Northern Ireland have been denied medical science for many years now. As you are aware, Northern
Ireland is part of the United Kingdom. I want to situate abortion in the
UK context. Last year (2008), as some of you know, the Human Fertilisation and Embryology Act progressed through the UK parliament.
The Act revises and updates existing legislation for assisted reproduction and makes changes to regulation and licensing of the use of embryos in research and therapy. The Act includes provisions of research
on types of embryos and changes the definition of legal parenthood
for cases involving assisted reproduction. For example same-sex couples are now recognized as legal parents of children conceived through
the use of donated sperm, eggs or embryos. However, one of the most
controversial elements of the Act was that of abortion and this is what
I will focus on.

There were 12 clauses relating to abortion representing both pro-
choice and anti-choice perspectives. The most controversial was the
proposal to reduce the time limit for accessing abortion (from 28) to
24 weeks. Those who supported that, pointed to other countries where
the limit is 20 or 12 weeks. Those opposed, said all recent peer reviewed
research showed that survival below 24 weeks gestation has not improved despite advances in other aspects of antenatal and the care of
premature babies. The vote was to maintain the limit of 24 weeks.

A further clause proposed putting stricter procedures in place where
women were considering for fetal abnormality but this was also defeated.

In October several amendments were proposed to the bill to mod-
ernize the law, improve clinical practice and women's access to abortion. What they wanted to do was to update the 1967 Abortion Act. But
the most controversial amendment was to extend the 1967 abortion
act to Northern Ireland. You may wonder if Northern Ireland is part of
the UK, why does the 1967 Act not include Northern Ireland? So, what
is the legal position?

Essentially, we are governed by a piece of Victorian legislation, the

1861 Offences Against the Persons Act. The 1967 Act was brought in to remove all the anomalies that the 1861 Act had produced. Northern Ireland has been left with it. This Act states that anyone procuring an illegal abortion will be kept in penal servitude in life. That is still the law in Northern Ireland. This law was brought in when Ireland was all one nation so the same Act also applies to the Republic of Ireland. If you can remember the penal servitude for life, that is significant.

When is an abortion legal in Northern Ireland? It is performed if the physical or mental health of the woman is at risk. That must be permanent and long term and probable rather than possible.

To understand why we have been excluded from the 1967 Act you have to understand the political context in Northern Ireland. As you know, we have emerged out of 30 years of conflict. So, intermittently over 30 years, we had direct rule from Westminster. Today we have a Northern Ireland Assembly which is male dominated. There are very few women. Religious fundamentalism is very apparent, it was mentioned yesterday on *Science* (March 5, 2009). When we elect politicians, we often do not elect them on social issues, but along orange and green lines. Orange if you are from the Unionist tradition and green if you are from the Republican tradition. That is how most people vote. Of the 102 members of the assembly, only two women will speak out from a pro-choice perspective. No man will speak. So, let's look at what the assembly debated. Let's look at extracts from what they have said.

In 1984, a Member of the Assembly stood up and said: "We have to leave the question of deformity in the providence of God and if a child is conceived in love, the parents ought to be willing to accept what God has ordained should be born to them. Even if it is deformed. It ought to be accepted as the will of God". And the next one: "Adolf Hitler had more charity in him than the abortionists. They would seek to put to death a child with no defects". And in 2000, nothing much changed: "One cannot rationalize explain away or excuse murder. It s is not saintly to promote legalization for abortion. It is more like an unblushing apology for mass murder. Greater access to abortion in our country will surely lead to a litany of broken hearts, ruined lives, butchered babies and the descent of the judgment of God. That price is too high". In 2007, nothing much again had changed: "As we look back we cringe at the number of Jews who were gassed or murdered by Hitler and rightly so yet in today's so called civilized society we witnessed 200,000 abortions across the UK last year which is 600 a week and 50 to 60 children an hour".

So religious fundamentalism is very evident. For example the wife of the First Minister is also a member of the Assembly and a Westminster Member of Parliament. She said homosexuality could be cured. And she knows a good psychiatrist who could do it and also said that pedophiles are better people than homosexuals. Her husband said, those were not the words of his wife, but of the Almighty.

We have members of the Assembly who were previously linked to paramilitary organizations who as you know were responsible for the deaths of hundreds of people for over 30 years. Many of them are antichoice. The peace process has allegedly been used to persuade the British government not to extend the Act. When the recent amendment to the bill was debated, it was clear that we were going to win that amendment. The leaders of the four political parties wrote to every Westminster MP urging them not to extend the Act to Northern Ireland. The leaders of the churches in Northern Ireland also wrote to every Westminster MP with the same message. Westminster MPs who supported the amendment were persuaded by the Government to withdraw their support and had to walk away from it. The members of the Assembly were debating the devolution of criminal justice to Northern Ireland. Allegedly they said: "If you do anything to the Act, we will walk away from the discussion and the peace process will be in danger of collapsing". Once again, women's lives were being used as blackmail.

Not one doctor in Northern Ireland will openly support the Act or abortion available in Northern Ireland. Not one doctor and not one scientist. I think we should be asking them why they are not doing it. There is not one member of the legal profession who will speak out. Not one.

In schools they say abortion is murder. They show films of fetuses thrown into buckets. They are taken out of school and sent on a day-long conference which tells them abortion is murder. This is the socialization process. Hard to get rid of.

Abortion is a problem that is exported. We had one organization which provided counseling for women. And 5-6 years ago there was an attempted arson attack on the building. We are now the only organization that provides counseling for women. We have protesters who stand outside the building four days a week displaying graphic distorted photographs of fetuses. Following women in the streets and calling them murderers. What are the consequences for women? Emotionally, they have to lie. Moreover, they have to go to England. They have to pay for abortion, 660 euro in the early stages. Even though they are members of the UK and they pay the same taxes. They have to pay this money. This rises up to 2,200 euro depending on the stage of the pregnancy. These are huge financial consequences for women. It has health consequences. What are women doing when they cannot afford 660 euro or 2,200? Many are purchasing early medical abortion pills on the internet. Some of the sites are rogue internet sites. The women are buying incomplete prescriptions. Or they lie and pretend they are over nine weeks pregnant. And we know of one woman who actually ended up having a ruptured uterus. There are also practical consequences. They have to fly. Some people do not have a driving license or passport to go on a plane. It has been recognized by Europe, but the British government has done nothing. Northern Ireland women are left with a Victorian law.

For instance there is the story of Mary. She was told that the fetus was no longer viable but she did not get an abortion. She had to find 2,200 euro very quickly to make sure she was in the limit. She had to travel to England to pay for a private abortion. That is the reality.

*Director, Family Planning Association, Northern Ireland

Laurence Bovy*
Assisted reproduction and research on embryos in Belgium

On behalf of my Minister, I would like to thank the European deputy and former European Commissioner Philippe Busquin for inviting her at this Congress.

I would like to recall that Belgium, with its medical team and researchers, has actively participated in the development of research and testing of new treatments for human reproduction. It would be pretentious to say that our Belgian teams were the earliest pioneers in the development of medically assisted procreation, although they have very significantly contributed to the development of this technique. In vitro fertilisation treatments are present in Belgium since the beginning of the 80's, we have so almost thirty years of experience behind. I would like to look back very briefly and show you how the Belgian legislative and regulatory framework has often evolved in order to adapt to the development of this technique.

In fact, we should admit that this development is usually more challenged when it occurs in private clinics with commercial purposes for luxury clients, as it happens for instance in California.

Since the late 80's, the Belgian health insurance partially refunds these techniques to patients in need and, in parallel, has developed a research based on funds coming mainly from the National Fund for Research, public and private partnerships and donations. Belgium, on initiative of the assisted procreation teams, has long been provided with a volunteer based register and since the 90's we have been publishing statistics of activities and results. These statistics show how the Belgian teams reached top level results. The legislator intervened only at the end of the 90's. As it usually happens, the legal framework is not synchronic with reality and it ends up following reality instead of anticipating it.

The first two elements pointed out by the legislator were the planning of the 1999 norm defining the maximum number of the assisted procreation centres allowed to operate in Belgium as well as the definition of their quality and responsibility rules. According to this norm, only public and university hospital centres are authorized to receive the status of reproduction centres, for which, of course, they have to fulfil also other requirements.

A new law was approved in 2002, through a negotiation within the health service sector, as social dialogue is extremely developed in Belgium - that defined the public funding of these laboratories in exchange for a norm setting the number of embryos transferred during in vitro fertilisation. The main purpose of this norm was to reduce the number of multiple pregnancies, mainly in defence of the public health but also in order to avoid the public welfare system to take care of the high number of premature babies often resulting from such pregnancies. Results were clearly visible and in return we could reinvest to reduce the cost that patients have to pay for these treatments. Nowadays the expenses of the patient are really modest as the health insurance covers most of the total cost. It is also necessary to consider that the multiple pregnancies rate has decreased of 50%. This way Belgium reached, together with Finland, the lowest multiple pregnancy rate of the world.

I would like to focus on two more laws. The first one is a law passed in 2003 on research on human embryos. It sets restrictive limits for the use of human embryos for research and therapeutic purposes: it defines the authorized laboratories, the possibility of experimenting only with less than 14-day-old embryos, the prohibition of an alternative on animals. The second one is a law passed in 2007 regarding the shared management of supernumerary embryos. When we talk about shared management, we want the patient to give his/her authorization.

In a small country like Belgium we perform between twelve and fifteen thousand cycles of in vitro fertilisation, so I would like to stress out the noteworthy results of our research. We apply spermatozoon microinjections in the ovule, the technique that revolutionized male sterility issues in the 90's.

A second element that is particularly important for my Minister, who fought against cancer herself, is the safeguard of fertility for women fighting against this disease. As you know, chemotherapy and radiotherapy destroy ovules in the ovary and often lead to sterility. Those are very sensitive issues. In two Belgian university centres two babies are born through spontaneous pregnancy after the graft of ovarian tissues taken and frozen before chemo or radio therapy. Those are two of the five babies born in the world from cancer-affected women. It is a spectacular progress in the research and a very promising project and we are proud of it.

I would like to leave you with a nice imagine. We think that research can be a source of hope and strength in our relation with life and future. Therefore I hope, even in such a short timeframe, to have well showed you what we have achieved in Belgium.

*on behalf of Laurette Onkelinx, Minister of Health, Belgium

The religious, bioethical and political approaches
to freedom of research

Marco Pannella*
**Religious, bioethical and political approaches
to freedom of research**

We have around an hour to tackle this subject, or better – we could specify – "religious, bioethical and political approaches to or against freedom of research".

Yesterday Mark Brown's contribution showed us how, as regards the problem, attitudes and positions may change in the move from the subject of "freedom" to carry out research to that of the "right" to carry out research.

I am now giving the floor to Alex Mauron. I believe that having among our speakers a professor from the University of Geneva has been a really wise choice, particularly because the case also provides a fine combination of the matters involved. We really could not do without a Swiss scientist, in this dimension of official Europe - of which Switzerland is not officially a part -, when it comes to discussing religious approaches - we should not forget that Switzerland is the land of Calvin -, ethics - in respect of which we should recall the ethics of Rousseau's justice - and politics. And in this case we find ourselves facing two opposing policies, since Switzerland is the only real example of federal and federation-based civilization as far as the rest of the continent is concerned.

As a final point, Professor Mauron talks about relativism, because so far it is always Benedict XVI who talks about relativism. Hence we will now hear the accused on the conflict between dogmatism and relativism, whereby anyone who is dogmatic hangs to the accusation of relativism those he would like to free himself from.

Professor Pervez Hoodbhoy is another essential presence because - and this may be just an obsession of mine - our numerals are Arabic, not Roman. An article published in the Turin newspaper *La Stampa* reminded us how important and overwhelming the contribution of Arab science was at an important moment in the civilization we would now refer to as "Western", although it would be better to say "European". We lived through a time when science and progress were Arabic and that gives me reason to hope that one fine day the dominance of English will fade and we shall adopt the international language, Esperanto.

However, the work of Professor Pervez Hoodbhoy is definitely more difficult, not in itself, but because we are here in these official and officious headquarters of an institutional Europe, which ought to recognise its Judaeo-Christian roots, by sidestepping the rest gained from the more recent history of our countries, along with the most ancient roots of the Mediterranean history of Europe.

In fact, I have the feeling that your efforts will be the greater. We are in debt not only of an Arabic science, but also an Arabic Europe, or as we would say now, an Islamic Europe, which was winning. It was not by accident that our splendid Roman numerals were cast aside in favour of a numerical system from that source and not being Judaeo-Christian, this would be rather hard to explain.

*Member of the European Parliament;
leader of the Nonviolent Radical Party

Alex Mauron*
**Epistemological relativism and religious dogma:
two strange bedfellows in the struggle
against freedom of scientific research**

Science and belief systems, be they religious or not, have regularly
been in conflict. In fact, such clashes antedate the rise of modern
science. Disputes about the relative standing of secular knowledge
and revealed religion were important issues in European universities
during the Middle Ages. At the dawn of science in the modern sense
of the word, the Galileo affair reached iconic status as regards the
science vs. religion struggles. It helped establish the epistemic independence of scientific knowledge and free the scientific research en-
terprise from the remit of ecclesiastical authority. Darwin completed
this emancipation process in closing the last gap in which theological discourse claimed explanatory power, namely natural theology
and the Argument from Design as applied to the living world. The
outcome of this phase of the conflict was the death of what might be
called "biotheology". Evolution and natural selection established biology on a firmly naturalistic foundation, an intellectual revolution
that still meets with considerable resistance today. The opposition
is actually on the rise, as evidenced by the diffusion of creationist
ideas and organisations outside of their homeland in the American
Bible belt, as well as the growing influence of Intelligent Design theory (ID), in circles beyond fundamentalist Protestant Christianity.
The unfortunate fact is that science, especially biological science, is
attacked more harshly by religious forces than was the case a few
decades ago. Yet the arguments brought forward by the religious opponents of science are by no means original and have been refuted
many times before. On the other hand, their tactical choices have
changed more or less drastically from earlier science-religion wars
and have become more sophisticated.

Today, opponents of science continue their struggle on two major
conflict areas between science and belief systems. The first is opposition against specific research practices, such as for instance the
derivation and study of human embryonic stem cells. As is well
known, many religious institutions, such as the Catholic Church, op-
pose this research. Contrary to a common perception, this opposi-

tion does not originate with any specifically religious ethical position, but from idiosyncratic – and mistaken - ontological assumptions about the nature of early human embryos, which in turn rely on obsolete, neo-scholastic, conceptions of nature and reason.

However, it is the second area of conflict between science and dogma which will be the focus of this essay. This is a struggle that is not mainly concerned with concrete research practices, but is being fought on the battlefield of culture, intellectual life, and social policy. In short, opponents of science try to marginalize science in contemporary life in three ways:

- by making it subservient to religious or non-religious dogmas;
- by "turning the tables" on science, i.e. by creating a mimetic pseudo-science that ventures to criticise real science on its own turf;
- by propagating popular relativism ("science is just another religion") in order to downplay the credibility of science, and to open an intellectual, political, and educational space for mimetic pseudo-sciences (such as creationism), as well as to attack public support for scientific research.

While the first move is not original and has been attempted repeatedly throughout the history of science, the other two are largely new and represent new dangers for which the scientific community is not always well prepared.

In the 150 years since Darwin's *Origin of species*, evolutionary theory has been hugely successful in all areas of the life sciences, from classical genetics, taxonomy, palaeontology, geology, biogeography, to more recent insight in developmental biology ("evo-devo", for instance), genomic taxonomy, immunology, infectiology, neuroscience... The list could go on and include many aspects of the social sciences as well. The evolutionary perspective has in effect become the mother tongue of the life sciences. This creates a situation in which traditional theistic religions have a difficult choice to make, a choice that is hardly less troublesome today as it was in 1859.

Either they move away from natural theology towards a theology that is more concerned with ethics and subjective religious experience, or towards a more abstract natural philosophy, such as theistic evolution. This is the stance adopted by many scientists who are also religious believers. It is also by and large the path taken by mainstream Christianity (but with qualifications, as we shall see).

Or religions fight back against modern science explicitly. This was the attitude of traditionalistic Christian churches in earlier times, which tended to reject science straightforwardly, as an impious and arrogant activity that the true faithful should leave aside. Today's religious fundamentalists are quite different. They are in fact much more aggressive and want to construct an alternative science that is supposed to be simultaneously "more scientific", more religion-friendly, and better attuned to traditional moral views. This is particularly the case of creationism and its variants, which provide a spectacular example of what I call mimetic pseudo-science, i.e. a pseudo-science that attempts to critique genuine science in the style (if not the substance) of scientific controversies, and imitates some superficial aspects of scientific life such as scientific-sounding institutes and museums, (self-appointed) experts, journals, and the like. creationism fights evolution, and therefore modern biology, on three fronts:

- biblical literalism: this is especially an issue for Young Earth creationism (YEC), who believes in a strict biblical inerrancy that includes the chronologies of Genesis
- natural theology and the validity of design arguments in biology: this (is) the special focus of Intelligent Design Theory (ID)
- the purported existential, moral and political implications of evolution: this is a concern common to all strands of creationism, and this is where epistemic relativism comes to the fore, as we shall see.

Although the focus here will be on the second and third areas of conflict between creationism and science, a few words on biblical literalism are in order. Firstly, it is to some extent a modern phenomenon. During early Christianity, the literal interpretation of Genesis was already controversial:

"For who that has understanding will suppose that the first, and second, and third day, and the evening and the morning, existed without a sun, and moon, and stars? And that the first day was, as it were, also without a sky? And who is so foolish as to suppose that God, after the manner of a husbandman, planted a paradise in Eden, towards the east, and placed in it a tree of life, visible and palpable, so that one tasting of the fruit by the bodily teeth obtained life?" (Origen, *De Principiis* IV, 3, 1)

From a modern creationist point of view, this quote sounds rather oddly sarcastic and if Origen, who lived in the beginning of the 4th century, were to be teleported into a contemporary American conservative protestant church and attempted to preach there, he would

most probably be kicked out! However, during the Middle Ages and
early modern times, biblical literalism seems to predominate and
even to co-opt the rising interest for establishing positive facts by
calculation. For instance, during the 17th century, there is increasing
interest for dating Creation using biblical genealogies. Archbishop
James Ussher dates the creation of the universe to the evening pre-
ceding the October 23, 4004 BC (as reckoned in the proleptic Julian
calendar, of course...). Biblical literalism is still strong in modern creationism (especially YEC and Muslim creationism). Even though the
literal account of Genesis never had any standing in serious science,
Young Earth Creationists have established a pseudo-science called
"Creation Science" that mixes the biblical text with the sort of naïve
positivism that was probably common in the 19th century and is still
embraced today by many technicians and scientists with little philosophical sophistication. Similarly, creationism is on the rise in the
Muslim world and its propaganda often emulates Christian creationist proselytizing efforts. The "Atlas of Creation", a beautiful coffee
table book promoting naïve antievolution views by an author with
the *nom de plume* of Haroun Yahya is sent out by an Islamic foundation to schools all around Europe. Recently, concerns for the rise
of Islam creationism in the West was raised by the British press:

> *"Leaflets questioning Darwinism were circulated among stu-
> dents at the Guys Hospital site of King's College London this month
> as part of the Islam Awareness Week, organised by the college's Is-
> lamic Society. One member of staff at Guys said that he found it
> deeply worrying that Darwin was being dismissed by people who
> would soon be practicing as doctors.*
>
> *"The leaflets are produced by the Al-Nasr Trust, a Slough-
> based charity set up in 1992 with the aim of improving the under-
> standing of Islam. The passage quoted from the Qur'an states: "And
> God has created every animal from water. Of them there are some
> that creep on their bellies, some that walk on two legs and some that
> walk on four. God creates what he wills for verily God has power
> over all things.*
>
> *"A 21-year-old medical student and member of the Islamic
> Society, who did not want to be named, said that the Qur'an was
> clear that man had been created and had not evolved as Darwin
> suggests: "There is no scientific evidence for it [Darwin's Origin of
> Species]. It's only a theory. Man is the wonder of God's creation.""*
> (*The Guardian*, February 21, 2006)

Islamic creationism seems more relaxed than "Creation Science"
about the earth being less than 10,000 years old and tends to accept

an interpretation of the "days" of Creation as being rather longish eras, but this in turn is also based on scriptural authority: "A day in the sight of your Lord is like 1,000 years of your reckoning" (Qur'an 22:47). It also uses arguments that belong to the second major creationist pseudo-science, namely Intelligent Design Theory.

Before we take a closer look at different forms of contemporary creationism, I should explain the concept of 'mimetic pseudo-science' as used in this article. creationism is not just like any old pseudo-science such as homeopathy, for instance. The latter positions itself outside the realm of normal science by denying the relevance of basic physico-chemical facts such as the atomic structure of matter, but more importantly by positing an idiosyncratic epistemology. As most other alternative medical theories, this perspective discounts populational and statistical evidence in favour of a strictly individualistic conviction that a particular treatment works for you. Evidence-based homeopathy is an oxymoron. Contrariwise, creationist pseudo-science is mimetic in that it puts great emphasis on being "truer" and "more scientific" than the conventional science put forth by the so-called scientific establishment. In fact, creationist discourse is constantly turning the table on science by critiquing particular evolutionary facts and insights in the name of a "healthy scepticism" that tries to emulate the inquiring and sceptical mindset of *bona fide* scientists. creationism tries hard to mimic the look and feel of real science, for instance by generating an institutional framework that resembles scientific institutions such as museums and "research institutes". For instance, the Seattle-based "Discovery Institute" has become a major source of ID material propagated in books, colloquia, and the Web. These institutions are busy producing critiques of mainstream science, but they generate no data. However much creationists purport to stand up to conventional science and claim success in terms of ordinary criteria of scientific truth. They utterly fail to transform their ideological commitments into actual research and the generation of new scientific insights. This illustrates the fact that, as is the case for other mimetic pseudo-sciences, creationism is a dead science. In contrast, living science is akin to a chain reaction. One major discovery generates more work to confirm or disconfirm it, which leads to new insights, new findings and so on... This snowballing effect never happens in a dead science, which merely expresses its bitterness against the "Establishment", yet is incapable of formulating, much less implementing, a research programme of its own.

Normally, obsolete scientific theories die of natural causes. For instance phlogiston theory was progressively superseded on account of the discoveries of 18th century chemists and was finally laid to rest by thermodynamics, without creating persistent and bitter controversies. Unless they are artificially revived for ideological reasons, obsolete explanatory frameworks in the natural sciences simply wither away once contrary evidence accumulates against them and/or they turn out to be incapable of explaining new discoveries. In contrast, one of the paradoxes of creationism is that it has been revived in the public sphere without having any merit as a basis for scientific explanations. In actuality, by the time of Darwin, biblical literalism had already been dead as a *bona fide* scientific view for nearly a century. The reasons were the realisation that the Earth is much older than is compatible with biblical dating (Hutton, Buffon), and the recognition of evolution as a scientifically explainable fact (Lamarck).

Why then were Darwin's views considered to be uniquely shocking for traditional religion? For an answer, we need to examine the philosophical underpinnings of theology that were dominant at the time, in particular the important role of natural theology and the Argument from Design. This argument had been part of Christian apologetics since Thomas Aquinas and before. By the early 19th century, while it had lost much ground as regards the physical universe, it was still part of conventional thinking in relation to the living world. It was widely believed that the purposeful features of living beings exist for a reason and that reason is ultimately provided by the planning activities of a divine architect. This was an essential tenet of the philosophy of religion of that time, particularly in Anglicanism. Of course, 18th century materialists such as the French *philosophes* had fiercely criticized this view, and David Hume had fatally deconstructed it in a more discreet but perhaps more effective manner. Yet in the absence of a fully-fledged alternative, it was still largely accepted. Darwin's theory of descent with modification and natural selection provided precisely that alternative. From then on, recourse to the supernatural was no longer needed to explain evolution and the adaptive features of organisms. Furthermore, Darwin's insight was in effect naturalizing the origin of humanity. It became clear that the human species is genealogically related to other primates, and that the origin of humans is explainable in essentially the same terms as the origin of any other species. In addition, as Darwin saw clearly, the evolutionary past of the human species is informative as regards many of its mental as well as physical traits. That insight is still widely unacceptable not only in fundamentalist belief communities, but in some mainstream religious circles as well, to the extent that they are still attached to one form or another of natural theology. Indeed, natural theology in its traditional formulation and the classical Arguments from Design are the hallmark of Intelligent Design theory. Today, ID theorists take a position that is very similar to the one advanced by those of Darwin's opponents who dismissed the naturalization of biology while accepting that some evolutionary change actually happened. Rather than denying evolution altogether, like Young Earth Creationists, they deny that random variation can have a useful outcome such as could explain complex adaptations of organisms. They believe that biological complexity implies a Designer, which they do not necessarily - or at least not openly - identify with the biblical God. In essence, ID theorists are pre-Darwinian because they stick to the Argument from Design as a scientific explanation.

ID theory is a mimetic pseudo-science, and just as dead as YE Creation Science. But it is more seductive, because it can be presented in a superficially secular disguise, and cannot as readily be dismissed as openly sectarian. This is why ID has some degree of influence in non-fundamentalist religious circles such as conservative Catholics. Official Catholic doctrine today accepts the reality of evolution and tries to avoid open conflict with modern science. This attitude is not merely tactical, as it is based on a philosophical conviction that asserts the existence of a single ultimate truth, encompassing both empirical and divine reality, so that any disagreement between science and religious teachings is thought to originate from misunderstandings. In actuality, the official belief in the concrete effects of divine Providence is a persistent problem and Catholic doctrine deals with it by redefining some aspects of science (the origin of the human mind, for instance) with a view to sanitizing them from their theologically uncomfortable implications. Evolution as fact is accepted, but recognizing the broader implications of natural selection for human nature and naturalistic accounts of human life and behaviour is branded as "neo-Darwinist dogma". The idea of a Designer is still influential and the current Pope believes that "an unguided evolutionary process - one that falls outside the bounds of divine providence - simply cannot exist". In fact, personalities close to the Catholic leadership have expressed opinions that are quite close to ID theory. Such is the case of the Archbishop of Vienna, Cardinal Schönborn, whose writings often evince many features of ID discourse:

"Now at the beginning of the 21st century, faced with scientific claims like neo-Darwinism and the multiverse hypothesis in cosmology invented to avoid the overwhelming evidence for purpose and design found in modern science, the Catholic Church will again defend human reason by proclaiming that the immanent design evident in

nature is real."

This quote includes several rhetorical moves that are typical of creationism. Firstly there is the charge that some scientists ("neo-Darwinists" and cosmologists subscribing to the multiverse hypothesis) have a materialistic agenda and are biased against evidence of design which is supposedly evident in nature. There is a whiff of conspiracy theory, too: scientists are presumed to be busy inventing theories with little scientific merit but whose purpose is to hide the signs of the divine presence in the world. Secondly, Schönborn links the recognition of design in nature with the defence of reason. This is a "turning of the tables" which is quite similar to the way ID theorists argue that materialist scientists are basically frauds, because "real" science, and "reason", are on the side of creationist conviction.

Opponents of evolution and the naturalistic study of life never really made an impression on scientific issues and never gained any respectability in scientific research. This however has not prevented their influence from growing. How come? One explanation that comes to mind at first is that they basically address a scientifically illiterate and generally "backward" public. This is not very convincing as it ignores the fact that for decades now, creationism has migrated out of the American Deep South into the wider world, and presently appeals to middle class individuals who are often technically educated. We have to turn to another, more plausible explanation, namely that science is not really the central issue here. Creationists' interest in science is superficial and their major concerns lie elsewhere. Indeed what they feel passionately about are not scientific explanations as such, but the moral, social, political and educational implications that they attribute to the choice between different views on evolution. In their mind, the ultimate falsity of Darwinism lies more in its supposed moral and social implications than in its scientific invalidity as they see it. In the words of R. Albert Mohler (Southern Baptist Theological Seminary):

"Evolutionary theory stands at the base of moral relativism and the rejection of traditional morality. If human beings are not made in the image of God, and if the entire cosmos is nothing more than a freakish accident, morality is nothing but a mirage, and human beings - cosmic accidents that we are - are free to negotiate whatever moral arrangement seems best to us at any given time. Human life has no inherent dignity, morality has no objective basis, and we are alone in the universe to eat, drink and be merry before our bones join the fossil record and we pass from existence".

The agenda of creationists is moral and political much more than it is scientific. creationists' writings are constantly insisting on the link they see between "atheist materialism" - which they more or less equate with Darwinism - and the moral decay and political disasters of the last hundred years. Again and again, creationist books and web sites depict Darwin, along with Marx, Freud and Nietzsche, as the prophets of the Antichrist, who destroyed the traditional commonsense view of the natural and social order. So creationism turns out to be closely aligned with reactionary political views, especially in the moralizing version so typical of the American Christian Right. It is this specific worldview that provides creationism with its ideological energy. It is also the real motive behind creationist efforts to influence school curricula, efforts that are expanding outside the United States, too. Epistemic concerns for critical thinking and scientific education are subsidiary to their real goal of advancing a religious, moral and political program in young malleable minds.

From the perspective of the history of ideas, blaming all the ills and tragedies of modern times on Darwinism is obviously silly and paranoid. It merely adds one layer of absurdity to creationist theories. More interestingly, a form of wishful thinking is inherent in this view. Indeed the basic paradox of creationism is that in order to fight the evil of "moral relativism", it has to rely on epistemic relativism. Something like a "relativistic syllogism" is an implicit but essential ingredient of creationism and goes a long way to explain its popular appeal. This syllogism could be stated like this:
  • premise 1: if evolution is true, there is no place for God in the natural and social order of things. Everything is random, nothing has meaning and we might as well despair, or indulge in mindless pleasures, do drugs, have wild sex, and so on...
  • premise 2: this is too awful to be true
  • conclusion: ergo it is false

However much creationists appeal to traditionalist commonsense against the Enlightenment and modernity, this syllogism reveals how much they are influenced by the popular version of modernity, or rather post-modernity:
  • "I adhere to belief X or Y because it makes me feel good"
  • "Science is just an opinion. It is the religion of materialist, hedonist ideologues"
  • "Science is just an opinion, so why should some so-called specialists tell me what is the case? This is a democracy, I will find out for myself what the case is, i.e. what it is I wish to believe"

These are the sort of relativistic platitudes that are so prevalent today. And far from opposing them, creationists use them cynically to advance their own ends. For instance, in debates about presenting creationist views in the biology classes of State schools (the foremost creationist agenda in the United States), their ostensible aim is to «teach the controversy» and to foster objective and free debate between contrary positions that are supposed to be equally plausible. This harks back to the rhetoric of political debate and is an essential ingredient of popular and media culture. Furthermore, this wishful thinking is present in many belief systems, including such that are not necessarily religious. Compare ID with the following anti-science ideologies that wield some influence nowadays:

- non HIV-based aetiology of AIDS
- anti-vaccine movements
- alternative medicine...

...and it will be obvious that they have a lot in common with creationism: sectarian passion, closed-mindedness, cynicism in propaganda, and a knack for ignoring or misrepresenting scientific findings. Their moral and political programme is often quite different from the conservative agenda of creationism, but the means that they press in the service of these views are very similar.

That is where the main danger to science in contemporary culture lies, rather than in any specific belief of creationism or of any other pseudo-science. The story of modern creationism illustrates that today, science is under fire from religious (and non-religious) dogmatic systems in ways that differ essentially from past science-religion conflicts. These dogmatic belief systems are much more aggressive than before, because they try to turn the table on science by imitating science. Moreover, wishful thinking is the driving force of these movements, because they are fuelled by the desire that science should be supportive of a particular set of values and ideals (traditional religion and conservative values in the case of creationism), more so than any genuinely scientific concern. Just as many other pseudo-scientific belief systems, creationism is at home in an epistemic relativism that is both essential to its tactics and fashionable in contemporary culture. More generally, creationism is one example among several of the current sacralization of belief over knowledge, a cultural force that is threatening to marginalize science in the context of education, health, and public policies, including research policy itself.

*Associate Professor of Bioethics,
University of Geneva Medical School, Switzerland

Pervez Hoodbhoy*
The battle for science and secularism in the Islamic world

I thank the organizers for inviting me to speak on a subject which, in my opinion, is of immense importance to global peace and security today. As a physicist who works in the field of nuclear and elementary particle physics, I have always been awed by the power of scientific reasoning. As a social activist, I am convinced that it is a vital tool for transforming human consciousness in a way that can lead to a more rational and humane society. Therefore, for the last 35 years, I have been teaching physics and popularizing science on television in the country where I was born, Pakistan. Whereas I still very much enjoy doing this, as well as physics research, I must confess to feeling disappointed at times.

Science in Pakistan, as well as in the Muslim world, barely exists today. No major invention or discovery has emerged from this one-fifth of all humanity for well over seven centuries now. This arrested scientific development is one important element - although by no means the only one - that contributes to the present marginalization of Muslims and their perceptions of injustice and victimhood. Such negative feelings must be checked before the gulf widens further. Today we face the prospect of a bloody clash of civilizations between Muslims and the West. Should the war actually occur, it will rank along with the two other most dangerous challenges to life on our planet - climate change and nuclear proliferation.

Scientific impotence may be one of the reasons why there is such a disconnect between Muslims and the rest. But let me first dispel the notion that Muslims are intrinsically backward or somehow incapable of modern thought. Unlike the native peoples of South America or Africa, Muslims have a rich history of contributing to global science and, to an extent, technology as well. Martians visiting Earth between the 9th and 13th centuries - the Golden Age of Islam - would surely have reported back to headquarters that the only people doing decent work in science, philosophy or medicine were Muslims. Muslims not only preserved the ancient learning of the Greeks, they also made substantial innovations. Mathematics, astronomy, chemistry, optics, mechanics, medicine, and human biology are some of the areas where path-breaking developments were made by Muslim scholars. This is a source of immense cultural pride.

But about seven centuries ago science and Islam parted ways. The modest rebirth in the 19th century has been eclipsed by a startling reversal away from science and modernity. This reversal began in the last decades of the 20th century and appears to be gaining speed.

Nevertheless, these days you will hear government heads and science ministers of Muslim countries make tall claims at conferences held around the world. They say that their countries are making great progress. Having attended a few such conferences, my impression is that the benefits lie mainly confined to the excellent meals consumed and frequent-flyer miles clocked up by the foreign delegates. Patents from Organization of the Islamic Conference (OIC) ountries are few. According to official statistics, Pakistan has produced only eight patents in the past 43 years. So what explains the slow pace of scientific development in Muslim lands?

Most Muslims angrily reject any claim that science and Islam are incompatible as idea systems. In the current epoch of growing antagonism between the Islamic and the Western worlds, they feel those accusations add yet another excuse for the West to justify its ongoing cultural and military assaults on Muslim populations.

In defending the compatibility of science and Islam, Muslims argue that Islam had sustained a vibrant intellectual culture throughout the European Dark Ages and so, by extension, is also capable of a modern scientific culture. The Pakistani Physics Nobel Prize winner, the late Dr. Abdus Salam, would stress to audiences that one-eighth of the Qur'an is a call for Muslims to seek Allah's signs in the universe and hence that science is a spiritual as well as a temporal duty for Muslims. But Abdus Salam, who I grew to know well and who wrote the preface to my book on Islam and science, readily acknowledged that the present intellectual climate in Muslim countries cannot sustain scientific growth.

The incontrovertible fact is that academic and cultural freedoms on campuses are highly restricted in most Muslim countries. At Quaid-i-Azam University in Islamabad, where I teach, the constraints are similar to those existing in most other Pakistani public-sector institutions. This university serves middle-class Pakistani students and ranks number two among universities belonging to the Organization of Islamic Countries, with 45 members. My campus has three mosques with a fourth one under construction, but no bookstore. Here, as in other Pakistani public universities, films, drama and music are frowned on, and sometimes even physical attacks by student vigilantes who believe that such pursuits violate Islamic norms take place. Islamabad, the capital of Pakistan, has no public library and no movie theatre.

As intolerance and militancy sweep across the Muslim world, personal and academic freedoms diminish with the rising pressure to conform. In Pakistani universities, the veil is now ubiquitous, and the last few unveiled women students are under intense pressure to cover up. The head of the government-funded mosque-cum-seminary in the nation's capital issued a chilling warning to my university's female students and faculty to cover their faces totally, else acid would be thrown upon them.

I want to tell you how hugely things have changed in my university over the three decades I have taught there. In rejecting science, Muslim orthodoxy has mounted a vigorous attack on the scientific method in recent years. It demands that the teaching of modern science in schools be correspondingly changed. So, for example, Newton's Law must no longer be called by that name. Nor should effect be related to cause. It should be noted, however, that the Iranian clergy has allowed science taught in Iranian schools to maintain its secular character.

Starting in the 1980's, the orthodoxy also posed an imagined "Islamic science" as an alternative to "Western science". This "science" claims that every scientific fact and phenomena known today was anticipated 1,400 years ago and that all scientific predictions can and must be based upon study of the Qur'an. This has been the concern of dozens of conferences in numerous Muslim countries, including Egypt, Pakistan, Malaysia and Saudi Arabia. Some religious scholars calculated the temperature of Hell, others the chemical composition of heavenly djinni. Still others triumphantly disproved evolution. But none produced a new machine or instrument, conducted an experiment, or even formulated a single testable hypothesis.

Religious fundamentalism is always bad news for science. But what explains its meteoric rise in Islam over the past half century? In my opinion, there is no one cause. But perhaps one cause is more important than all other causes combined. Although this conference has carefully avoided issues that directly relate to politics, I must clearly tell you that, in my opinion, the huge acceleration in Islamic fundamentalism has fundamentally to do with global politics and the pursuit of power by powerful nations.

To make my case, let us go back to the mid-1950's. At that time all Muslim leaders were secular, and secularism in Islam was growing. Iran under Mohammed Mossadeq, Indonesia under Ahmed Sukarno, and Egypt under Gamal Abdel Nasser are examples of secular but nationalist governments that wanted to protect their national wealth. What changed subsequently? Here the West must accept its share of responsibility for reversing the trend. Western imperial greed subverted and overthrew them one by one. Standard Oil did not want Mossadeq, so he went. The CIA hated communists, so Sukarno went. And so on.

At the same time, conservative oil-rich Arab states - such as Saudi Arabia - that exported extreme versions of Islam became US clients. The fundamentalist Hamas organization was helped by Israel in its fight against the secular Palestine Liberation Organization as part of a deliberate Israeli strategy in the 1980s. Where weak secular governments collapsed, or were subverted, a vacuum was created. Nature, as we all know, abhors a vacuum. Islamic fundamentalism and its promises rushed to fill the vacuum.

Perhaps most importantly, following the Soviet invasion of Afghanistan in 1979, the US Central Intelligence Agency armed the fiercest and most ideologically charged Islamic fighters and brought them from distant Muslim countries into Afghanistan, so helping to create an extensive globalized jihad network. Today, secularism is continuing to retreat. Inept and unpopular governments in Pakistan and Afghanistan are providing enormous impetus to the Taliban who are sweeping over the two countries.

How can science and secularism return to the Islamic world? I have no silver bullet to offer. Forward movement will require global justice become a priority. Colonialism is no longer acceptable. The United States must give up their Bush-era dreams of total planetary control and abandon PNAC, the Project for the New American Century. Instead of seeking "total spectrum dominance" in space, air, sea, and land, it must learn to live with the rest of the world. In this respect, the election of Barack Obama is to be welcomed as a harbinger of change but his administration will have to work hard to change the common opinion among Muslims that the US is at war with Islam. So far he is not doing enough and had no comments to make when, two months ago, as American jet fighters flown by Israeli pilots dropped bombs over the world's largest slum and killed hundreds of children. Such deaths feed into a bitterness that could lead to a never ending war of civilizations.

Progress will also require behavioral changes among Muslims. If Muslim societies are to develop technology instead of just using it, the ruthlessly competitive global marketplace insists on not only high skill levels but also intense social work habits. The latter are not easily reconcilable with religious demands made on a fully observant Muslim's time, energy, and mental concentration. The faithful must participate in five daily congregational prayers, endure a month of fasting that taxes the body, recite daily from the Qur'an, and more. Although such duties orient believers admirably well toward success in the life hereafter, they make worldly success less likely. A more balanced approach will be needed.

Science can prosper among Muslims once again, but only if there is a willingness to accept certain basic philosophical and attitudinal changes - a *Weltanschauung* that shrugs off the dead hand of tradition, rejects fatalism and absolute belief in authority, accepts the legitimacy of temporal laws, values intellectual rigor and scientific honesty, and respects cultural and personal freedoms. The struggle to usher in science will have to go side-by-side with a much wider campaign to elbow out rigid orthodoxy and bring in modern thought, arts, philosophy, democracy, and pluralism. Science cannot prosper under authoritarianism. And authoritarianism runs deep everywhere. It underlies the conventional Muslim family structure that demands absolute obedience, and a tyrannical educational system where the teacher crushes independent thought. Muslim women must be given the same rights as men. Without intellectual and personal freedoms, Muslim societies shall continue to suffocate.

Fortunately, respected voices among believing Muslims see no incompatibility between the above requirements and true Islam as they understand it. Progressive Muslim forces have recently been weakened, but not extinguished, as a consequence of the confrontation between Muslims and the West. For this both sides are blameworthy, the proportion of which can be endlessly debated. But what cannot be denied is that on an ever-shrinking globe there can be no winners. It is time to calm the waters. We must learn to drop the pursuit of narrow nationalist and religious agendas, both in the West and among Muslims. In the long run, political boundaries should and can be treated as artificial and temporary, as shown by the successful creation of the European Union. Just as important, the practice of religion must be a matter of choice for the individual, not enforced by the State. This leaves secular humanism, based on common sense and the principles of logic and reason, as our only reasonable choice for building the world's societies and nations.

*Professor of Physics,
Quaid-i-Azam University, Islamabad, Pakistan

The geopolicy and the future of genetic,
regenerative and reproductive medicine

Giulio Cossu*
The new theraphies ahead: promises, challenges and risks

This is a period of rapid progress in biomedical research. Therapies that were not even conceivable thirty years ago are now a clinical reality, with many more in the pipeline. There are hopes for patients affected by as yet incurable diseases but there are also many obstacles and risks.

In my talk I will not address the obstacle represented by the dogmatic and anti-scientific attitude of the Vatican, as this issue has been and will be addressed by others in this meeting. Instead, I will discuss the many additional problems that even new therapies not dealing with embryonic stem cells will have to face. These can be summarized as follows:

- risks for the patient's health deriving from uncontrolled clinical trials
- risks for the progress of research due to excessive regulations
- excessive costs of these new trials.

I will try to demonstrate that a balance between these two opposite risks and efforts to cut the cost without compromising on the quality of the treatment may be the key to success.

Recently the International Society for Stem Cell Research has published *The Guidelines for Clinical Translation of Stem Cell Research* (http://www.isscr.org/). These Guidelines "provide a roadmap for the responsible development of safe and effective stem cell therapies for patients. They call for rigorous standards in the development of such therapies including stringent evaluation and oversight, a thorough informed consent process, and transparency in operations and reporting" (Hyun et al., 2008). As a member of the Task Force that wrote these guidelines, I experienced the difficulty of writing this document, where almost each word had to be weighed very carefully. On the one hand it was mandatory to suggest rigorous controls to make new procedures as safe as possible; on the other hand it was felt that pushing the controls and the rules too far would lead to an arrest of medical progress.

Stem cells are not distinguished from progenitors by any physical feature and still poorly by the antigens they express, so that the only reliable criterion of identification is their biological activity, that in vivo can only be assessed retrospectively. This means that anybody can claim to work with stem cells and pretend to obtain a biological and/or therapeutic effect, with little chance to be controlled in advance. The explosive proliferation of private clinics all over the world that promise therapies for any incurable disease and are the target of "stem cell tourism" is in part due to the above considerations. Warnings against these treatments by academics will have little consequence on people who are desperate and see the disease progress daily, taking more and more of their life or that of their relatives.

A few weeks ago, we learnt that donor cell-derived tumours had grown in the Central Nervous System (CNS) of a young teleangectasic patient, transplanted with human fetal neural stem cells in a centre in Russia (Amariglio et al. 2009). We do not know and are obviously worried about the consequences of this situation for the patient and for those who may be treated in future. The limited information available on the nature and the characterization of the transplanted cells (Poltavtseva et al. 2003) makes it difficult to predict whether this event is a consequence of inadequate cell characterization or may in the future occur also in the most rigorous and controlled trial. As an obvious and general rule, the cell population to be transplanted should be characterized in deep detail; if fetal or embryonic in nature, strategies should be implemented to prevent uncontrolled proliferation of transplanted cells or kill them if necessary. Also possible contamination by infectious agents should be checked in great detail. Other issues such as survival, proper differentiation and functional integration in the transplanted tissue are crucial for the success of the transplant but less relevant to safety.

At present time, much of this information about the cells transplanted in the patient is not available and so it is very difficult to draw conclusions. Still this case should warn all the patients travelling to distant countries to be treated with stem cells. This warning does not depend on the arrogance of Western academics labelling anything beyond their own science as unworthy: approximately thirty years ago a new treatment for Acute Promyelocytic Leukaemia was initiated in China with retinoic acid (vitamin A) and soon was repeated in the whole world to become the standard treatment for this disease (Nowak et al. 2009).

The problem with these "stem cell clinics" is the total absence of records, follow up and publications of these trials. We saw on television one patient claiming that he felt much better after the treatment and could even do movements that he could not do before, but we know nothing of objective evaluations, functional measurements, and the overall outcome of the treatment. We also ignore the exact nature of the cells, how they were prepared and checked for purity, ability to perform the requested functions and absence of contamination. Under these circumstances there are significant risks involved in a journey that will cost a lot of money, raise false hopes and may even be dangerous for the patient.

It may be objected that things in the "official science world" move too slowly for patients whose disease progresses rapidly. This is true but unfortunately there is no faster way to proceed, other than the uncontrolled ones discussed before. Why is progress apparently so slow, at least based on a patient time? Because it is necessary to do all possible controls to make sure that the new therapy is safe and effective, although problems may occur even with the most rigorous controls in place.

Six years ago, an unpredictable, severe, and adverse event in a trial of gene therapy for children affected by a congenital immune deficiency led to severe restrictions in the clinical use of genetically corrected hematopoietic stem cells, and to heated debates on the safety of retroviral gene transfer vectors (Williams and Baum, 2003; Gaspar and Thrasher, 2005). Since then, five out of twenty children treated in two different clinical trials developed T-cell leukaemia that in one case was fatal (Hacein-Bey-Abina et al. 2008; Howe et al., 2008). Could this have been prevented by more pre-clinical work? Probably not, because the problem had never appeared in any of the animals treated with the same procedure during preclinical investigation. Could more in depth analysis of the effect of retroviral integration in the human genome have provided useful information? Possibly, but it should be considered that the sophisticated technology currently used to look at viral insertions into the human genome did not exist at the time, and that the wealth of information now available on the subject would not exist, had those adverse events never occurred. Most important, it should be kept in mind that the majority of the 31 patients treated with gene therapy for two forms of lethal congenital immunodeficiency are now alive and well only because of this "risky" therapy (Hacein-Bey-Abina et al. 2008; Howe et al., 2008; Aiuti et al., 2009). To put this in numbers: 5/31 is 16% of morbidity and 1/31 is 3% of mortality. For cancer chemotherapy, this would be an unbelievably fantastic result. For gene therapy, people insisted that these therapies should be stopped. It is now conceivable, following the case of the patient from Israel, that many will ask for a halt to therapies with stem cells until further evidence is accumulated. How can this be achieved if patient trials are stopped? Critics may not remember that many of the first patients receiving bone marrow transplantation (BMT) did not survive (Thomas, 1999). They may not consider that, with current regulations, none of hundreds of thousands of patients who received BMT would be alive today. Therefore, given that precautions are rigorous and trials controlled as much as possible, tests on new therapies must continue.

One final point concerns costs that at present are extremely high, assuming that no profit will derive from any of these trials and that patients will not be asked to pay for the treatments. Costs are generated by several causes: first, the pre-clinical work, especially when protocols have to be tested on large animals affected by the same disease (i.e. haemophilic or dystrophic dogs), to which must be added the cost of toxicological studies (where cells or viral vectors are considered "drugs") carried out in authorized centres. Second and often crucial is the cost of cell or viral vector preparation under GMP/GLP (Good Manufacturing/Laboratory Practice) conditions, in specialized centres where the real cost of cell preparation is many times higher than in a normal laboratory. In essence, the same criteria for safe drug production are applied to cells, which is total nonsense for two simple reasons:

- there are probably not two identical cells in the body and to pretend that they are always identical to each other in different preparations implies a complete ignorance of the basics of cell biology;
- a drug is distributed to millions of people while cell treatments are very few and often for single patients so that the level of risk for "errors" is clearly on a different scale. Additional costs relate to a number of procedures that have to be implemented (Advisory Board, Data Managing Board) and to hospital costs.

To give an idea, for a first trial with progenitor cells in three patients affected by Duchenne Muscular Dystrophy 2,5 million euros may not be enough. Should one of these trials work, who will pay for the many other patients who are eligible? Although premature, this problem may have serious future consequences in respect of patient access to possible therapies. Eventually it should be possible to cut costs without compromising on the quality of the treatment.

The challenge of these new therapies is ahead of us and we should prepared to cope with both predicted and unforeseen problems: rational solutions are available and possible.

* Division of Regenerative Medicine,
San Raffaele Scientific Institute and Department of Biology,
University of Milan, Italy

Miguel Kottow*
Why the Third World needs its own view on science

Ever since Galileo used a technical device for his scientific endeavors in astronomy, science and technology have been inextricably
fused in a symbiotic relationship that has led to an unprecedented
expansion of knowledge and instrumental power. It is not surprising
that this development made technoscience increasingly dependent
on external circumstances. The freedom of scientific activity, still a
cherished goal, has been subject to critical analysis and to the reluc-
tant acceptance that external contingencies can constitute the necessary material support, but also the source of unwanted pressure
that modern science must deal with. Science can be understood as
pursuing its goals in the wake of side constraints that have become
transcendental to it, that is, they are unavoidable conditions that
make science possible. Side constraints are boundaries within which
a scientific goal is pursued.

Since the beginnings of modern science, when limits imposed on
science were embodied by the authority of the Church, contingencies have increased due to three factors. One is the already mentioned fusion with technology which, being always an applied
activity, must take into account the social environment where it un-
folds. A second reason that limits the expansion of technoscience is
the growing influence of political, economic, environmental policies. Finally, recent decades have witnessed an increased emphasis
of research focused on the life sciences, to the point that one can
speak of bio-technoscience as a realm where risks and benefits need
to be more critically monitored. Two additional factors that influence the degree of freedom science may enjoy are the internal ethics
of professional scientists and the truth validation of scientific knowledge. Scientific explanations will be true if and as long the scientific
community accepts them as such (Peirce) and provided they conform to current forms of deliberation and style of thinking (Fleck).
Professional ethics of research and the validation of truth claims are
intrinsic and therefore unalterable limitations of scientific activity,
only to be mentioned in this paper.

Side constraints that are external to science are contextual in nature and therefore more or less unavoidable; they vary from one society to another and throughout time. It is therefore more than probable that science in affluent societies will show a different pattern of side constraints than Third World nations. Economic constraints limit the amount of material resources available and, perhaps more important, show sponsors to earmark their support by requiring the pursuance of specific research topics, e.g., military financing of nanotechnology. Economic constraints become abusive when vested interests dominate and condition their support by imposing a certain line of research and dictating what should be investigated and how research results are to be handled. Closely related to economic side constraints are those set by pragmatism, represented by the quest to obtain patent-worthy results or to seek knowledge that will make products more attractive to the market. Considering that trials have migrated from universities and research institutes to commercial COMs (commercial research institutions) and SMOs (site management organizations), it is hardly surprising that the for-profit motive of science becomes predominant. Social discrimination constitutes a third side constraint, when studies are designed to support preconceived prejudices - the search for a gene of homosexuality - or research arbitrarily selects certain groups or topics, e.g. neglect of female pathology or paucity of studies linking poverty with disease. Social discrimination on a large scale is best illustrated by the fact that some highly damaging epidemics like malaria are receiving little scientific attention, having become part of a group of similarly unattended diseases known as "neglected diseases". A fourth cluster of side constraints comes from public issues that try to reinforce certain forms of political power, like Nazi Germany`s development of "racial" biology, the search for correlations between race and IQ, or the focus of public health on bioterrorism. Political aims have also influenced scientific activity when competitive factors are at issue: nuclear arms races, development of satellites and space-ships. Ethical evaluation and priority-setting will try to influence research policies towards promising therapeutic lines of investigation or, on the contrary, divert efforts from such research as appears to some extent threatening: cloning, nanotechnology, biological weapons. The Asilomar moratorium on genetic research is an example of ethical constraint. Ethical issues that become ideological lose all credibility, exercising a form of unacceptable censorship, as has been applied to embryonic stem cell research. Any social practice, science included, is abused when limitations are issued on the basis of beliefs that are not universally shared and therefore cannot be imposed. Dogmatic positions are the enemies of scientific freedom, as they are of any other social activity like teaching, the arts or politics.

Although inevitable, side constraints are amenable to negotiation, so that highly qualified scientists and prestigious centers of research may liberate themselves from contextual policies and be allowed to determine their own research agenda. By the same token, less developed countries will face limitations not only inherent to scientific activity per se, but also to an exacerbated influence of political, social and economic factors. Poor countries have become the preferred turf of First World sponsors that relocate their research interests in regions where ethical controls are less demanding and research subjects are easier to recruit. The external funding of such studies reflects the interests of sponsors and often leave little or no benefits to local research subjects and communities. Consequently the scientific concerns of neglected host countries must be met by their own research efforts in order to broach local problems and needs. Local science so comes under an additional side constraint, namely the need to finance research that is relevant to its society. Criteria of relevance must be applied to set a priority ranking, since resources will only be available for the more immediate and pressing problems. Relevance is a much resisted side constraint to scientific activities, especially by external sponsors who set their own priorities in oblivion of local host needs. Scientist working in disadvantaged settings will often become accomplices in neglecting the local relevance of their research efforts, focusing as they do on securing grant monies and participating in the quest for prestige and peer recognition obtained by publishing in journals of high impact. Of direct concern to the ethics of research is the opposition to ranking and funding research projects according to relevance because, it is argued, there is no objective way of doing so. The relevance of a project can be gauged in two ways. An investigation can be directly pertinent to a pressing social problem, as exemplified by epidemiological studies in a country plagued by some highly prevalent disease. This is the kind of external relevance that can be readily evaluated and classified as social relevance. On the other hand, when evaluating a research project in the less practical, say archaeology or musicology, relevance can be judged if peer reviewers recognize that a project will be significant in the advancement of the discipline - cognitive relevance. Admitting that this is not a fool-proof approach, it nevertheless can qualify as an attempt to acknowledge that societies have a right to evaluate what is being done with their money, and it brings us back to the essence of science, which is not the impudent curiosity that got Adam thrown out of Paradise, nor the pure admiration for nature that inspired Aristotele, but a strategy to improve man's adaptation and survival in a world that may not be hostile, but is utterly indifferent to human concerns.

The increasing migration of scientific projects to less developed host countries, raises some ethical questions concerning the recruitment of research subjects, especially considering a number of papers that are suggesting an universal obligation to participate in research programs. Some believe that research aims at the common wealth and ought to be generally supported, to the point that even incompetent human beings are to be recruited as research subjects. Another argument suggests that in nations where citizens enjoy the benefits of a national healthcare system, they are under the moral obligation to participate in research efforts. Harris advocates universal participation based on two arguments: everybody should take part in projects aimed at averting harm and producing benefits. Secondly, since medical advances benefit all those who eventually will need them, it is only fair to collaborate in their development, lest one should be at fault as a free-rider. The logic of these arguments has been put to task, and some additional objections arise from the vantage point of disadvantaged populations. Science pursues interests that not necessarily include the common wealth. Such occurrences as the 90:10 divide of resources and research goals, the existence of neglected diseases, the tendency to pursue lucrative patents and "me-too" drugs, make evident the predominance of vested interests that cannot claim universal support. Furthermore, research sponsors have been unwilling to share benefits with the individuals and communities that have been instrumental to their research results. If universal participation is expected, it should enjoy the retribution of an equally generalized sharing of benefits.

Coming back to the original title of this round table discussion, "the geopolitics and the future of genetic, regenerative and reproductive medicine", an initial remark is that there is no geopolitics of medicine but rather a geostrategy. Rather than prospective policies, strategies are short term choices of utilitarian goals, which immediately brings up the question equality, between those that benefit from these goals and those who do not. When medical research and practice seem to aim beyond therapeutics objectives, a semantic analysis is required to either dismiss from the medical realm all non-therapeutic aims, or to expand the arena of medical concerns to include such interventions as physiologic or even genetic enhancement. Is enhancement to be seen as genetic medicine? Is sex selection a form of reproductive medicine? Does prolongation of life expectancy belong in the realm of regenerative medicine? If they are medical endeavors, should not priorities be set regarding the urgency of disease control? If they are scientific non-medical endeavors, should not the relevance of medical versus non-medical biological interventions be evaluated? Can we neglect the question of relevance if we are confident that science is the answer and that a great number of pressing questions remain unsolved? Unless we hold on to an infinite optimism à la Bacon, expecting science to eventually untangle all the problems that plague mankind and to develop ways of solving them, it will be necessary to continue performing science as usual, that is, pursuing specific interests, and accepting certain unavoidable side constraints. Ideology should not interfere with science, but stakeholders need to accept that the common wealth is not to be neglected in the name of private interests. Hopefully, they will consider what classical utilitarianism is about, namely, that the best be done for the most.

*Universidad Diego Portales,
Universidad de Chile, Santiago, Chile

Stephen Minger*
**Therapeutic and research potential of human
pluripotent stem cells**

I am grateful to Marco for the invitation. I have found this meeting to be very, very interesting, as I have heard some of the best intellectual discourses all together in one time. So I am happy to be here.

Particularly in response to some of the presentations held yesterday, I have really changed the focus of what I should have been talking about. So I will briefly touch on the therapeutic and research potential of stem cells. But I also want to tell you a little bit of a story till the end, which I think is a tremendous successful story for science, in particular about the legislation that has been changed over the last three years in the UK. As it is, I think this story is actually emblematic of how much power scientists really have. But it requires a huge amount of deferring and scientists have to learn how to fight if they want to change religion and dogma and government perspectives. So I will take you through this rules scenario.

First of all, let me say that in my lab, like many others, we have been focusing on the use of stem cells for many years now. I myself have been a stem cell biologist for 20 years. This lays out what we do. So a lot of our work is devoted towards developing cell therapy, that is pluripotent cells. But we use other stem cell populations as well. And we are very agnostic with regard to stem cells. Therefore we focus on clinical application. And we go for the best, most available population we can.

We are interested in trying stimulation in tissues, working on the adult nervous system, where they can be mobilized. We try to understand how this happens and if we can exploit it, having in mind new therapies for the brain. In fact we think that if we can develop technologies which allow us to differentiate into very specific cell populations, we can also use those cells in fundamental drug discovery.

The real problem with Big Pharma is that their drugs screens are based on the use of tumor cells or primary cells and that leads to a lot of drugs that end up in phase 2/3 and then fail, and that is a part of the reason why it costs so much to develop new compounds. On the other hand, by using pluripotent cells we can differentiate them into a wide variety of different types of cells and we can use those cells as new screens for drugs. So we are eventually using human cells as defined cellular populations to develop new therapies. And, last but not least, we can also use these to – and this is the real point that I want to talk about – develop what we call disease specific cell lines, or rather human embryonic stem cells that include disease-causing genes. And that I will save for the end, because it leads into a nice story.

First of all this goes just to show you that there are a plethora of different stem cell populations. Really we think that in the course of their development we have the most potent stem cells. Then, as the development proceeds, stem cells become more and more restricted in terms of their ability to give us different tissue types. Anyway, as professor Cossu pointed out, the dogma has now changed. And we, too, think that nowadays it might be possible for development processes to actually go backwards, because at present with induced pluripotent cells we can take other mature differentiated cells, and with exhausting genetic engineering at a current time we seem to be able to take them backwards in time and take them to embryonic stem cells.

Nevertheless, the field is rapidly developing. New stem cell populations are being found all the time. We, together with our colleagues, showed that in the adult male testes, for example, there appears to be a stem cell population that looks like embryonic stem cells as well. We hardly know what these cells do, nevertheless they seem to have all the attributes of a few many other stem cells.

We have stem cells from fat, stem cells from baby teeth, stem cells from toe nails... There are stem cells everywhere. We work on all of them. We make no distinction between all these types of populations. As for me, I am a scientist, I am not a moralist, and I work on what I need for clinical applications. Now I think these cells are the cells that have the most fierce utility for us.

Embryonic stem cells are derived from the very early human embryo. They are the very first cells which arise in development. We can take these cells out of the developing blastocyst at a time before which they express any indication of any specific tissue. You can put these cells into culture and under conditions that we still do not really understand - these working conditions were developed back in the 1980s - these cells will expand to very, very large numbers, without aging.

These cells run like any other cell population in the human body, because they never get old. They just keep growing and growing and growing. We have had cells in culture continuously for years and they just keep expanding and yet they retain the ability to differentiate into all these different cell types. Today we do not know of any other cell population that can do that, although the induced pluripotent stem cells may be very analogous to this behavior. But without cells derived from early human embryos, we do not really know what induced pluripotent stem cells are, and whether or not they have the same capabilities as the human embryonic stem cells.

Now, I am fortunate to work in a very enlightened environment. In the UK we have some of the strictest regulations around the derivation of the human embryonic stem cells. And that really grows out of a very long history of regulation of reproductive medicine.

So Louise Brown, the first test-tube baby, the first IVF embryo was born in the United Kingdom in 1978. IVF was a technology that was developed by the UK medics Bob Edwards and Patrick Steptoe. After Louise Brown's birth there was a huge amount of controversy about IVF. Was this playing God? Was this leading to designers of babies. Was it eugenetic engineering of embryos, braving the world, *1984...* and all of that. Then there was a lot of debate and discussion, which led to which was called the Warnock Commission meeting in 1985. And the major recommendation from that consultation was that the UK should establish a regulatory body to regulate reproductive medicine.

Parliament took that suggestion and in 1990 we enacted the Human Fertilisation and Embryology Act which led to the Human Fertilisation and Embryology Authority. Every clinic in the UK, were they public or private, are now regulated by this authority. And they had to obtain a license for every procedure which they might perform within that clinic.

Because IVF is notoriously inefficient and very large numbers of embryos are derived on account of it, but will never be used clinically, it had been recognized since the early 1990s that there would be literally thousands of unused embryos. I will explain why, in a moment or so. Because of that, since 1991 it has been permitted to use human embryos for research in the UK. And today some 20,000 embryos have been used for research since then. But this is not trivial.

In order to gain a license from the HFEA (Human Fertilisation and Embryology Authority) before 2001, you had to prove to the authority that the research you wanted to do could only be done with human embryos, not with mouse embryos or cow embryos or anything other than human embryos. The research had to specifically address the following five research sectors: Treatment of Infertility;

causes of congenital diseases; causes of miscarriage; development of more effective conception; improvements in preimplantation genetic diagnosis. And the research had to be necessary or desirable. But: what does "necessary or desirable" mean? Anyhow, this is how the authority would make a decision...

You all do notice that you cannot, for example, use human embryos for cosmetic testing. You cannot use them to test food additives. Neither of those uses are necessary and they are not desirable. That was the *status quo* up until 2000 or so. And then Jamie Thompson and others developed some of the first human embryonic stem cell lines. After that they were trying very hardly to get access to those cell lines, which was difficult because these groups were just ever the first in the world and researches were struggling to learn how to grow those cells. Secondly, there were hundreds of research groups who wanted those cells and it was clear that it was going to be years before cell lines were made available.

The UK government pushed through what is called the extension of the Act. In 2001 both Houses of Parliament added to the five original research areas three new research areas where one could use human embryos. And that was meant to lead to a better understanding of human development, to a better understanding of disease processes and to develop new therapies for human diseases. These latter two areas allowed me and my colleagues in 2002 to apply for a license for a line of human embryonic stem cells. Together with Austin Smith's group, we got one of the two licenses in force in the UK.

What you hear from me is the real picture of the ethical environment in which I work. We are allowed to approach couples, either at the time that they are undergoing a consultation about IVF or are going to make a decision about what to do with embryos, because in the UK you can only freeze embryos for five years. At the end of that period, the couple have to make a decision about what to do with those embryos. Usually the decision boils down to this: should I have them destroyed or donate them for research? Most couples who have kept them, have completed their fertility treatment. So they are not going to use them. Rarely they will donate them to other couples. So, the real distinction is again: do I have to destroy them or donate them for research? That is the reality of embryo donation.

In the UK couples can donate them under consent. They are not given inducement for donation. They do not get half-price IVF. As a matter of fact, they sign away all rights to any cell line which may be developed. They cannot dictate how they are to be used; nor have any control whatsoever over them. We let them know that the cells may be used commercially. And that someone may make a lot of money. And that they go to a Big Pharma company, where they may develop a drug out of them. Not a single penny will ever come back to the couple. Therefore they have no reason to donate embryos, except for the fact that they rather see them used for research, than destroyed.

One of the other things that came out of the new legislation in 2002 was the stipulation that anyone who is granted a license to derive human embryonic stem cells is required to place the corresponding cell lines into the UK Stem Cell Bank, where they are available to any researcher in the world, as long as the research they want to carry on is ethical and sound. Our research lines have been exported to Italy. But unfortunately the Italian colleagues cannot use our lines, because they do not get funding to support that research.

Somatic cell nuclear transfer which is commonly referred to as "therapeutic cloning" using human eggs is legal in the UK, but we completely banned reproductive cloning in 2001. Let me point out that all of these points are not guidelines. They are statutory. If I violate any of these rules, for example if I were to offer someone money for their embryos, or if I would implant embryos that I made by cloning into someone's uterus, I would go to prison for 10 years. That is true for anyone who is licensed by HFEA. And there are severe penalties if you step out of license. What I think of is really the model system about how to do ethically contentious research where you have very tied, very rigid regulation, versus one system that is scientifically permissive. I will show how this has changed over the years.

This is the scene in 2002. This is how you make human embryonic stem cells. We have done this, like a certain number groups worldwide. This is routine IVF: normally the first day – that is immediately after fertilisation - before the *nuclei* are fused, you keep the embryos in culture. You usually grow them till day 3. And then they are implanted. In the UK, unlike Italy, you cannot implant more than three embryos. In most cases only two. The remaining high-quality embryos are generally frozen. And the number of high-quality embryos depends on the number of eggs you start with.

It is not uncommon for women following supra-population to have 15-20 eggs. So any other high-quality embryos which are not implanted are frozen and, as I said, can only be stored for five years currently. In order for us to make stem cell lines, we obtain that they are generally frozen at day 3. We culture them until day six, and the reason of this day 6 is the formation of that entity called blastocyst.

This population of stem cells here, 20-40 cells, this is what turns into you and me. This is the inner cell mass that will go on to turn into the fetus properly. The larger structure is the placenta. In most cases we remove the inner cell mass, put it into culture and derive individual lines of embryonic stem cells. Each line is unique. It comes from a different embryo, and has its own genetics. One line is genetically different from any other line. All of these cell lines are capable to turn into a wide diversity of cell types. They make lung, heart, liver, pancreas, skin, muscle...

They make every cell type we ever looked for. The idea is to take them into clinical applications. This is a list of the things we work on with our lab collaborators, trying to take cells and trying to learn how to differentiate them into cell populations, reproducibly day in and day out, in that scale, because as the professor pointed out, in order to take these cells to the clinic, we have to generate very, very, very large populations of cells, in order to be able to treat the huge number of patients who will benefit from these therapies.

Now I want to shift to making what we call "disease specific cell lines". This is the generation of human embryonic stem cells which encode known disease-causing genes; that is genes which, when mutated, give rise to genetic disease. In 2006, when we proposed the work I am going to tell you about, there were only three ways that one could do that. Of these three ways, one consists in relying on embryos which have been screened by pre-implantation genetic diagnosis, which is used for couples who are fertile, but who have a risk of passing on a known genetic disorder to their children. An example of that may be a couple who are both carriers of cystic fibrosis gene. Neither of them is affected. But they have a 1 in 4 chance of having a child which will have cystic fibrosis. Then they undergo IVF. On day 3, when the embryo is at 8-cell stage, the embryologist will remove a single cell from each of the embryos and diagnose those embryos for the presence or absence of the specific disease-causing gene. Those embryos obviously are not used clinically and in general they are discarded. Therefore, as the Clinical King's is one of the world leaders in pre-implantation genetic diagnoses, we easily recognize that these embryos are a source which present problems, and they are to be destroyed, although they represent a tremendous cellular resource.

So, for example, if you can take a cell line which encodes the cystic fibrosis gene - this is the first cell line that we made this way - and if you can differentiate those cells into human lung cells, it gives you a cell population allowing you to begin to try to understand how it is that these deranged proteins interfere with the normal cell function.

The idea is to try to create a model disease in a dish. And because human embryonic stem cells can turn into every cell type, each in-dividual cell line can be used to differentiate those cells into the cells more specifically affected in any individual disease. The problem with PGD embryos is that you get very few of them, because most of these diseases are somehow rare and secondly you never know if you are going to get embryos. Some couples will donate those af-fected embryos, some will not. So it is not certain that you are going to get embryos with these disorders.

The second way is scientifically quite complex, but basically what you try to do is taking a normal cell line which is free from disease and then replace the normal gene with the muted gene. The idea is to take a normal cell line and introduce a disease-causing gene into it. The third way is a more defined and more accessible way of doing it, which is very simple: it is cloning.

The use of somatic cell nuclear transfer to create cloned human embryonic stem cells is pretty simple. I may use Marco as my exam-ple. Cloning involves eggs. You have a source population of eggs, maybe left over from IVF. And you remove the nucleus from the egg. In doing so you remove the genetic identity. At the start, the woman donated the egg, then you take out the DNA from the woman. So you have now an empty egg, because it has no genetic identity whatso-ever. Then we will take a skin cell from Marco and put it into the egg, give the egg a little bit of electricity - you do not even need sperm for this - and a considerably high proportion of the egg will begin to di-vide. And then we will give rise to an embryo, just like an embryo which has been created by IVF. From that embryo I can take out the inner cell mass.

And then I have a population of pluripotent DNA cells. Forget this nonsense debarment of putting them back to the patient, because it is totally unrealistic. The strength of that lays now in the fact that the cell line has Marco's genome in it. Every cell that we create from this cloned embryo will be genetically matched to Marco. If Marco had a genetic form of Alzheimer's disease, that cell line now has that ge-netic disease. So cloning is a way of creating cell lines from living human patients that you can induce to become pluripotent stem cells that we want to be used for disease ends and would allow us to specifically select known individuals who have a genome when in-terested in creating very specific cell lines and very specific individ-uals.

Well, this is great. A great idea! Yet there is just one small problem. Where do you get eggs and how many eggs do you need to be able to create a cell line? In 2005, many of us were thinking about this. We thought this would be easy. We had a friend who had showed how to do it. This is my friend, professor Hwang from Korea in 2004. In his lab in South Korea professor Hwang was the rock'n'roll superstar of stem cell biology. This guy was it: a supreme scientist in Korea, 60 million dollars from the Korean government to do his cloning work, also flying first class all over the world. That was it. This guy was good. And the reason why they were good to him and his équipe is that they were the world's best cloners and still are by a mile.

What people do not realize about Hwang and his group is that Hwang is a veterinarian. All his career had been based on cloning livestock. They had hordes of pigs that had been genetically engineered to provide tissues or organs as a bridge for human transplantation. They had hordes of cows genetically engineered so that they could not be infected and give rise to BSE (bovine spongiform encephalitis). He had cloned dogs. Actually, his is still the only group in the world that has successfully cloned dogs. They cloned wolves. They were trying to clone Korean tigers. He even paid the Russian mafia two million dollars for some mastodon DNA, but unfortunately it did not work.

These guys were running a factory. It is estimated that they did between 2 and 3,000 nuclear transfers a day, every day, seven days a week, 365 days a year. And they had been doing that for years. When Hwang first reported that they had successfully cloned a human embryonic stem cell line from 250 human eggs, we all believed it. Look at the expertise that was there: simply astounding...

When he subsequently, one year and a half afterwards, reported that they had improved the efficiency to 10%, we all were wowing over completely. Probably everyone in this room was, as this was simply astounding. Maybe we are not as good as Hwang, and we might need 50 eggs to create one cell line, when Hwang needs ten. But we now know that it was all not true.

Hwang's group used over 2,200 human eggs from young women, many of whom in his own research group. They did not make a single embryonic stem cell line, a single cloned line. With all their expertise and with the best eggs you are ever going to get, they went right from the ovary into nuclear transfer. If Hwang could not do it with 2,200 fashionably obtained human eggs, how many do I need? If the efficiency is 1 in 10 and I said I should need 50, that means that I should need 10,000 eggs to make each cell line. How many young women in this room would be willing to come in, undergo this super-ovulation, have a needle inserted through the uterus into the ovary aspiring some eggs for my research work, when I need minimally 10,000 to make each cell line?

This could not be ethically justifiable. Much more so, as I and Armstrong - who was also my colleague in Newcastle - had a better idea. We would do what Hwang did, that is we would bring on the cows. Our argument was something like that: what you need is an egg, it has not to be a human egg, because if the argument is that, when you remove the nucleus from the egg you remove its genetic identity, you also remove its species identity. There is no longer a cow in a cow egg that had its nucleus removed. So we have a cow mytocondria, but there is no cow. The cow has gone.

If you take a human cell and you transfer his/her skin cell into this ex-cow egg and it makes an embryo, it has to be a human embryo. It is not half cow and half human; it is not a cowboy; it is not a mutant; it is a human embryo. The mytocondria are going to be hybrid. There will be a small residual population of about 20% which will be hybrid, which, based on previous work in China making these embryos from rabbit eggs, does not interfere with normal function. This is where we were in 2006.

Hwang's fall from grace happened very, very rapidly by the end of 2005. In February 2006, the national university completed its investigation, discovered none of the cell lines were real. In fact, they all were fake. And he was disgraced. We had a press conference in London, where we tried to have a retrospective on what this meant for the field of stem cell research and regenerative medicine. At that press conference many of us were asked: if Hwang could not do it with his huge number of eggs, what are you going to do? Lyle (Armstrong) and I said categorically that no one should be using human eggs. We should only be using an alternative source. And we proposed cow eggs. The headlines of the newspapers went crazy over this. But we were serious about it, as this was not a joke. And so in November 2006, Lyle and I filed the license applications to the HFEA.

This meant that the scientists were going to the regulators, saying: "Regulate us. These are human embryos. They fall under the HFEA act. And we want a license to be able to do this work". But we did not start the work. There was a lot of discussion about "are these truly human embryos or not"? And we argued that they were. We might have been cowboys, as somebody pointed out, but we were not. We decided that we would go through the process of getting a license to pursue this work, rather than starting it. The problem was that the government was not receptive.

Over the previous year the government had been looking at revising the original 1990 Act and bringing it up to date with changes in reproductive medicine and changes in stem cell biology; and it was going to be a new Act. They released the consultation a month after our license application and they categorically said that they would ban all this research. There would be no cowboys. All hybrid embryos would be banned. This was rather interesting. Why? Why are you going to ban this? If these are human embryos, they are no different from other embryos. So, the scientific community was not happy about it. Nobody wants its own research to be banned. Additionally, we were not given good reasons to support the banning. It was said: "I cannot understand why anyone wants to do it". The problem is that the HFEA is an independent regulator, free from the government influence, and the government is trying to tell them what to do. There was a rally, and in January - two-three weeks later - we had a huge press conference in London and we defended ourselves.

Moreover, a group of prominent scientists including five Nobel Prize laureates in an open letter to the *Times* said to the Prime Minister: "This research can be regulated like any other research and should not be banned". The HFEA at an open meeting said they were not certain what the status of the embryos was, that is, whether they were human or they were not. Rather than making a decision about what to do with our license application, they did the proverbial time-out in Britain and they went to consultation. They said they were not going to make any decision with our license application, but would wait until the consultation, which would take at least eight months. We could have challenged them legally because the HFEA, by statute, has to make a decision in three months. We could have forced them to take up a decision. But we decided that we would go through the process and see where we came out the other side.

At about the same time, the Select Committee on Science and Technology in our House of Parliament - which is committee of about 15 MPs who all have some depth of interest or are scientists or medics advising the Parliament on issues regarding science and technology – decided that they would have their own investigation. Over the spring they had a huge consultation. They invited hundreds of people: scientists, bioethicists, lawyers, religious people, nurses, everybody who had an opinion came in. At the end of this, all unanimously said that these were human embryos.

Do go online and look at the select committee's report. It is thick. It is one of the few Select Committee's reports where all of them agreed that this research should be funded. The HFEA later that summer came to the same conclusion. They were human embryos, they fell within the HFEA Act. Therefore our license application could go off for peer review and in January 2008 we were granted our licenses.

If that would be the end of the story, it would have been a tremendous triumph for science, because we won. We had confronted the government from the opposition and through rational discourse, pragmatic consultation, got them to reverse themselves. But we got something even better than that, because soon afterwards the government proposed a new bill, a new human fertilisation and embryology bill that started its way through Parliament.

Then at Easter, on Good Friday - I do not know if it is like that in Italy, or in the rest of Europe, certainly in the history of the UK - everybody disappeared and went on holiday. And the Cardinal could not have done this any better. As a matter of fact, on Good Friday he released his Easter Sunday Sermon, saying this research was monstrous, was grotesque, and that he expected the Prime Minister not to put this bill through. Moreover, if the bill would go through, he demanded that individual MPs had a free vote, because Catholic MPs, as well as other people in the cabinet, were saying that if they could not vote out of conscience on this bill, they would walk out of the cabinet.

We got caught completely unaware. There was nobody from the government to defend us. Robin Lovell-Badge and I spent the whole Easter weekend on TV, on the radio, in the newspapers, trying to fight this off. The new Minister of Public Health Dawn Primarolo came back from holiday immediately afterwards and said: "I want three things from you. One is: I want to come and visit your labs. Then I want you to make me understand better this research. Thirdly, I want you and your colleagues to get into parliament and fight for this bill". Because what was in the bill by then was really pretty interesting.

In addition to the cytoplasmic hybrids, which was the little bit of research we wanted to do, which was taking human DNA and putting it into an egg which had its own DNA removed, the government decided they were going to wrap in primary legislation a number of types of hybrid or high-mixed embryos, including, at least in principle, that you could make a true hybrid, that is taking human sperm or egg and fusing it with non-human sperm or egg. This was really contentious, because when the first three went through in votes, all the first three were voted in favor by three to one.

There were a lot of people who really opposed the true hybrid embryo. And many people told that the government was actually encouraging people to try to create this, but this was not the case. The government was putting this in the legislation so that you could not do these true hybrid without a license. I do not really understand why people were freaked out about this. As John Harris pointed out, we had had humanimals for quite a long time. Hybrids had been there for a while, but nevertheless this proved really controversial and yet the bill was passed by a margin of about 80 votes.

We were told over and over again by very conservative MPs that they had voted in favor of this because the scientific community had gone into the parliament and spent hundreds of hours with MPs, working with the Minister's team getting this legislation through. And so that bill is now law. And hybrid embryos are well within that. Now, I am often asked why this happened. This is the reason why - the scientific community took on the government and did not just disappear.

They did not say: "I will go back to my lab and dream of something else". They fought back. We stood up and fought. We had a huge amount of support from really prominent scientific societies: the Royal Society, the Academy of Medical Sciences, the Wellcome Trust, the Medical Research Council. The heads of these organizations would come into parliament with us. We had support from over 300 patient organizations and charities who would write letters to the *Times*, urging the government to push this legislation through. They played their own role, trying to convince the MPs to vote for this. The news coverage in general was extremely good.

We had the major scientific journalists on our side. There were the usual headlines like "crazy scientists" in the tabloids. But in the *Times*, the *Guardian*, the *Independent*, the *Telegraph*, the real science writers in Britain were very supportive and they did a great job in educating the public. The consultation process I think was absolutely crucial, because the government initially was afraid that there was a huge public opposition to this, but what they discovered was that 60-70% of the people were in favor of this.

Moreover the HFEA's own consultation showed that if you initially identified people who were opposed to it, generally on grounds of a religious kind, 60-70% of those people would change their mind when they were better informed. A lot of people would say: "What is the problem? We do not see that there is a problem as long as it is regulated. Regulate the hell out of it. Make the scientists accountable, but do not block fundamental research". I think it was the Minister Dawn Primarolo who was really crucial in this respect, because she was determined to get this bill through parliament. But she would not have done it without the support offered by the scientists.

*Director,
King's Stem Cell Biology Laboratory, London

Neuroethics:
challenges and opportunities

Piergiorgio Strata*
Introduction to the neuroethics

Neuroethics is becoming a very important topic in the field of neuroscience. I will introduce today's two speakers with some preliminary concepts about the topic.

When we are discussing ethics, do we only use rationality, or do we also involve an emotional component? Can we dissociate them? In the last few years, this topic has been intensively investigated by means of new technology that allows to watch inside the human brain in an non-invasive manner when a person is thinking or deciding. The results obtained are also important in other areas, like decisions on how to buy something like a car or a perfume. This field belongs to the neuroeconomics.

Philosophers have always discussed whether emotions guide ethical decisions or whether ethics must be driven by rationality: who is right and who is wrong? In our brain we have areas serving rationality and others that are involved in emotions. Look at the dorsal part of the brain, it deals mainly with rationality; below it is the ventral part, which is active when we are happy or sad or afraid. An important part of this emotional brain is an area called insula. The insula is activated, also when one is witnessing anger.

In order to study the role of rationality and emotions in our ethical decisions, let me now describe three experiments.

First experiment. On the left side of the figure you see a car which is running on a track where there are five working men. You have a switch in your hand and by pressing it you may deviate the car on another track where there is only one person. I tested this old dilemma with my students for many years and asked them whether it was ethically acceptable to press the switch and kill one person to save five. As reported in the scientific literature, over 80% of my students were in favour of pressing the switch. Then another paradigm was asked: the same car is running under a bridge, and you may now save the five working men by pushing a person close to you down from the top of the bridge onto the car's path to stop it. 10-20% of the students now said that this decision was ethically unacceptable. This very old philosophical dilemma has been posed recently to persons while taking images of their brain. The results have been published in *Science* of 2001 by Green and collaborators. What came out from this paper is that when the first dilemma is posed then only the rationality area is activated, but when the second dilemma is posed the emotional areas are also activated. This experiment shows that rationality cannot be the only criterion of moral decision and emotions are also involved. More recently, in a paper published in *Nature*, it was shown that patients with a lesion to the insula are more inclined to accept to push another person on the track, which means that, with less emotions, rationality plays a stronger role.

Second experiment. This is quite simple: you tell people that a brother and sister who never had sex decide one day to try sex between them. They take all precautions to avoid pregnancy, and do it just to have the experience. Almost everybody says that this behaviour is ethically unacceptable, but nobody is able to provide a rational explanation when asked, and when they were repeatedly asked they said: "I do not know why it is wrong, but it is wrong". This is typical of emotional behaviour.

Third experiment. I am now going to illustrate the so-called 'ultimatum game': I give Marco 100 euro and tell him that he has to share the money with Kathinka (Evers). Both of them know that the game is played only once. Marco gives Kathinka as much as he wants. However, if Kathinka refuses the donation both of them lose all the money. In other words, Marco has to give enough money to make her happy in order not to lose everything. The experiment shows that if Marco gives 50 euro, there is no refusal, because this is a fair share of the money; the same behaviour is evident even if Marco donates 40 or 30. However, with smaller donations, the majority of people like Kathinka refuse the offer and nothing is gained. If you now look inside the brain of the receiver during the game it is interesting to see that when Marco is offers Kathinka 10 euro, she gets upset. She does not say anything, but there is an activation of the emotional centres. Rationally speaking, Kathinka should have accepted any amount of money as it is better than nothing, but emotions were driving her decision.

These experiments show that our brain is wired to punish an unfair behaviour even at our expense. Other experiments of this kind also show that our brain is wired to promote cooperation and altruism, the way to live together in a fair way, and punish selfish behaviour.

Let me add an interesting experiment published on *Neuron* a few weeks ago: if rationality and emotions are so important in our decisions, how can a judge in the court be fair in punishing people? Scientists looked at the brain of judges when they had to condemn someone: what they said was that when judges decided whether somebody was guilty or not, then only the rational mind was active. However, when they had to decide the severity of the punishment, then the insula came into play and there was a tendency to moderate the punishment. To conclude, moral decisions depend on both rationality and emotion.

*Scientific Director,
European Brain Research Institute;
Co-President, Luca Coscioni Association

Kathinka Evers*
Towards a philosophy for neuroethics:
informed materialism and the naturalistic responsibility

The 21st century has seen neuroscience develop rapidly and a new academic discipline emerge: neuroethics, the attempt to explain moral judgment in partly neurobiological terms. It is useful to distinguish between fundamental neuroethics, researching how knowledge of the brain's functional architecture and its evolution can deepen our understanding of moral thought and judgment, and applied neuroethics, dealing with ethical issues that arise, e.g. in neuroimaging techniques, cognitive enhancement or neuropharmacology. Neuroethics inspires hope as well as apprehension and historic awareness is essential in order to determine the nature and *raison d'être* of this young research area. The aim in this presentation is to present neuroethics together with a dynamic model of the human brain and mind upon which neuroethics can fruitfully be constructed.

Historically speaking, threats to scientific freedom have come from religious or political forces. Notably, the sciences of mind were blocked for centuries by the Catholic dogmas, e.g. of the human immaterial soul. However, during the 20th century, the threats to this part of scientific development did not primarily come from religious forces, but from science itself. When at long last, by the end of the 19th century, mind science was at last free to study the human brain and mind, mind science developed psychophobia.

Scientific theories about human nature and mind in the 19th and 20th centuries were occasionally caught in two major traps: ideological hijacking and psychophobia, notably in the form of naïve eliminativism, and naïve cognitivism. To avoid them, neuroethics needs to build on the sound scientific and philosophical foundations of informed materialism, that:

- adopts an evolutionary view of consciousness as an irreducible part of biological reality, an evolved function of the brain and a suitable object of scientific study;
- acknowledges that adequate understanding of conscious, subjective experience must take both subjective information obtained by self-reflection and objective information obtained

from anatomical and physiological observations and measurements into account;

• depicts the brain as a consciously and unconsciously autonomously active, plastic, projective and narrative organ evolved in socio-cultural-biological symbiosis; and

• posits emotion as the hallmark of consciousness. Emotions made matter awaken and enabled it to produce a dynamic, flexible and open mind. As depicted by informed materialism, the neuronal person is truly awake, in the deepest sense of the word.

The relevance of neuroscience to explaining the evolution of moral thought presupposes a model of the mind and the brain that takes variability, emotions and creative thinking into account. According to informed materialism, the brain is a variable, selectional system in which values are incorporated as necessary constraints. Biologically speaking, no creature with a brain is born value-free; it is neurobiologically predisposed to develop these complex and varied systems of values that enable it to function in its physical and social environments. In this model, the human propensity for passing moral judgment and capacity to perform free and responsible moral choices do not only make logical and practical sense but are biologically unavoidable for adult, healthy individuals. The theoretical and methodological relevance of neuroscience to ethics is strong and fast developing. According to the theory of neuronal epigenesis, socio-cultural and neuronal structures develop symbiotically with mutual causal relevance. The architecture of our brains determines our social behaviour including our moral dispositions, which influences the types of society that we create, and, *vice versa*, our socio-cultural structures influence the development of our brains. This is compatible with the position that norms cannot logically be derived from facts on pain of committing the "naturalistic fallacy". A major challenge of fundamental neuroethics is to decipher this network of causal connections between the neurobiological and the socio-cultural perspectives; to evaluate the "universal" values pre-specified in our genome and shared by the human species, in distinction from those that stand related to a given culture or symbolic system. The "fallacy" of the naturalistic approach so becomes inverted into a responsibility.

*Associated Professor,
Senior Researcher at the Center for Research Ethics & Bioethics,
Uppsala University

Eric Racine*
**Neuroethics: tackling the ethical and social challenges
of the neuroscience revolution**

Thank you for inviting me; this is an honour and a delight. I have
been learning a lot about European debates related to science, politics and ethics in the last two days. I really learnt a great deal from
the talks I have been attending, and I feel a particularly strong connection with the topic of scientific freedom. This relates to the place
where I work as a researcher, the IRCM - Institut de recherches cliniques de Montréal, which was created by one of our leading Canadian physicians, Dr. Jacques Genest, who is an international leader
in hypertension and the author of several hundred publications.
Genest was a firm believer in scientific freedom: his motto, whenever he recruited new researchers, was to find the right people, to
back them up, and keep out of their way. He had a strong commitment to scientific freedom but he was also a pioneer in developing
bioethics in my country: his decisions led to the creation of the first
Canadian bioethics centre directed until recently by Dr. David Roy.
Genest set an example of how scientific freedom needed to take into
account ethics and social issues. So, while listening to the talks in
the last days, I have tried to identify some areas that relate to the
topic of this panel (neuroethics) and that reflect challenges and opportunities created by neuroethics. I think there are several of them
and I will highlight two of them right now, which we can discuss together afterwards.

One challenge is the shape of the responses to ethical questions
created by neuroscience, especially in terms of scholarship and policy: neuroethics is one form of response, and we shall debate and
discuss this model. The other challenge relates to one of my main
areas of research, public understanding of neuroscience and public
information about science, a theme we have come back to over and
over in the past two days. I think the question of how to transfer science to the public is complicated: we would like to think it is simple,
but it is complicated. I will show data that indicate how neuroscience, for example, is creating both excitement and confusion. This
of course can be problematic because we have to keep in mind that

the misunderstanding of science can create and fuel fears and un-justified ethical concerns.

My own approach is based on the belief that we need to engage with ethics and social issues proactively: it means that these issues are not simply fears, they are challenges, potentially, and we have to find solutions to tackle them. The transfer of research to healthcare is something that I think we have alluded to in the last two days. We like to entertain a simple and idealistic view of the relationship between science and society. I will now use the work of a famous scholar of science communication, Dorothy Nelkin, to highlight that this cannot be the case. She says: "The way people perceive research and interpret costs and benefits may be influenced less by the details of scientific evidence than by media messages." This is concerning for many of us, I think. Also, something else in the back of my mind is the relationship between liberty and scientific freedom, on the one hand, and the ethical obligations created by the conduct of research, on the other – I will come back to this.

First, I wish to spend a few words on neuroethics, which consti-tutes a response to the neuroscience revolution: I will try to describe this revolution by using three examples of different neurotechnolog-ical applications that are creating a lot of debate and ethical chal-lenges. One of them is neurostimulation as a form of neurosurgical innovation; the second is neuroimaging research; the third is neu-ropharmacology and its potential use as a form of cognitive en-hancement. In a few minutes I will highlight what I think are some of the responsibilities we need to enact as we move forward, in terms of neuroethics and the neuroscience revolution.

Neuroethics has been defined in different ways, and the following is by my colleague Judy Illes and me:

"Neuroethics is a new field at the intersection of bioethics and neuroscience that focuses on the ethics of neuroscience research and the ethical issues that emerge in the translation of neuroscience re-search to the clinical and public domain. Although there are lively discussions on the nature of this new field, the single most important factor supporting it is the opportunity for an increased focus and integration of the ethics of medical specialties (neurology, psychiatry and neurosurgery) and of the ethics of related research to improve patient care."

This definition, among others, highlights neuroethics as an ethics of neuroscience research and of the ethical issues that emerge in the translation of the neuroscience research to the clinical and public domains. Accordingly, neuroethics is considered an opportunity for

an increased focus and integration of the ethics of medical specialties to improve patient care.

My approach is pragmatic and, for me, neuroethics clearly has
practical goals, but I recognize by saying this that there are many
other goals pursued by neuroethics. Neuroethics is also viewed as
an opportunity to promote dialogue and public debate as well as a
way to address basic lingering healthcare needs of specific neuropa-
tient populations. I will be focusing on two of these multiple goals
of neuroethics during my talk: one of them is to tackle challenges
created by advances in neuroscience and neurotechnology; another
is to promote public dialogue.

With regard to the neuroscience revolution, the first example I will
discuss occurs in the field of neurosurgery, that is the use of deep
brain stimulation (DBS), which is a form of surgical stimulation that
has been used in over 35,000 people to treat Parkinson's disease and
is helpful to diminish tremors but does not represent a cure. For example, DBS does not solve some of the common psychiatric problems related to later stage Parkinson's but it is a very interesting and
promising therapy pioneered in France in the 1990s. There is now a
growing interest in a broader application of DBS in psychiatry, but
the cost of the device and its surgical implantation is approximately
35,000 euros. We have talked about access to technology in the past
days; and we are dealing with the example of a technology that is obviously not available to everyone even though it has been clearly
shown to be effective. The underlying issues here are the profit and
economic interests underlying the evolution of neurodevices,
proven to be one of the most profitable areas within medical devices.
There is nothing necessarily wrong with profit making but the problem here is restricted to the sharing of the technologies which, in
turn, ensures access to the therapy.

Another issue with DBS is that amongst the many studies of science in the media that I have conducted, I have never seen such
hope and so much hype about a neuroscience technique. For example, we have identified that there is a growing amount of news coverage of neurostimulation in the US and UK: the headlines are very
optimistic, and in a way they do not convey the reality of DBS. As I
mentioned, DBS is being tried now in clinical trials in numerous psychiatric conditions, for example, one target is major depression,
which is not treatable through psychotherapy, pharmacology or
even electroconvulsive therapy. This serious form of depression can
respond to DBS, based on a few recent studies, which is very
promising, though as I mentioned there are resource allocation issues and public understanding problems.

The second example illustrating the neuroscience revolution relates to the field of functional neuroimaging. There are now a few techniques that capture brain responses when a volunteer or a patient performs a task. This is not structural imaging where you will identify a structure, but a type of imaging that measures brain function and activity. There are various strategies or techniques that are used, such as PET scan (Positron Emission Tomography) and EEG (Electroencephalography). One technique that is increasingly used, at least in research, is fMRI (functional Magnetic Resonance Imaging), because it is non-invasive and studies can be repeated or conducted in more vulnerable and elderly populations. This graph, in its upper segments, shows how from the 1990s to the early 2000s the proportion of fMRI research studies dealing with topics we have discussed in this panel increased, that is neurosocial studies examining how the brain responds to moral judgment, empathy, deception and lying, as well as judgments on race, and neuroeconomics. These studies account for a growing proportion of fMRI research, this is not something necessarily or intrinsically bad, but rather quite exciting and interesting. The problem is that this research, strictly speaking, has not remained within the realm of science: it is becoming applied science and is leading to uses of this technology beyond a research context. One example is No Lie MRI, based in San Diego, which sells fMRI as a new type of lie detection technique: in the US there is certainly some interest in this form of fMRI use.

The problem with such uses of fMRI is that, at this point in time, we do not have the research to support them. Studying lying and deception is highly complicated: you have to take into account potential differences between lying in a natural context and an artificial environment like a research lab. You also have to factor in the difference between various forms of lying, such as deliberate lying, concealing information, or simply not remembering the details of a crime scene. These forms of lying and deception could involve different brain systems and cognitive processes; at this point in time it is difficult to reliably detail them with fMRI and, therefore, difficult to identify if someone really is lying or deceiving. There are many other applications of fMRI: one of the underlying issues is obviously the premature application of science and, as we saw, this can do a disservice to ethics and science. Another recent application, from September 2008, is the use of brain scans in India to incriminate individuals: this is a very debatable use of imaging but it is nonetheless occurring.

Now, a piece of data from my own research is a study that examined neuroscience innovation in the print media of the US and the

UK: over 1,250 news pieces were analyzed and we found many things, including problematic science reporting. However, some of the most interesting findings were qualitative in nature and involved three emerging interpretations of neuroscience. The first one was neuroessentialism (in a nutshell, the belief that we are our brains and that neuroscience is dealing with this), which raises the stakes prematurely and may create fears. The second one was neurorealism, that is, that neuroimaging techniques can provide forms of mind reading, even though these only measure indirect brain activity (such as brain metabolism or brain oxygenation) rather than the activities of neurons *per se* and there are several issues associated with the scientific project of measuring, localizing, and mapping the activity of thousands of neurons (this is an ongoing and unfolding science, and the kind of claims that we are finding in the media do not necessarily reflect our progressive understanding of brain function). The third one, which I think may be more interesting for this audience, was the use of neuroscience to inform decision making policy and lifestyle choices, that is, neuropolicy, which could evolve in different ways. With regard to the latter, I selected one example from a right-wing group in the US who approached a researcher to use fMRI to show that pornography is addictive. There was a clear political agenda behind this request and there are some groups wanting to finance this and other research to find brain activity patterns that relate to what they want to convince you of. So, this is a really interesting process that is happening here and I think it clearly calls for broader approaches beyond the academia and to engage in policy-making.

The third example of the neuroscience revolution I want to spend time on is cognitive enhancement. I learnt yesterday that this topic is being discussed in the European Parliament. Cognitive enhancement includes the use of drugs and other interventions to modify brain processes with the aim of enhancing memory, mood and attention in people who are not impaired by illness or disorder. This issue has been gathering media coverage such as this example from *The Economist* of last spring. It summarizes some of the expectations regarding smart pills such as the belief that we will be able to simply pop pills and be smarter. If it could be this easy, it would be terrific. Seeing this you may think: is our speaker describing some kind of science fiction? Is this happening and should we be concerned about this? Perhaps. Data from a *Nature* poll published last spring show that in over 1,400 respondents, 20% reported having used cognitive enhancers, slightly more than for medical use, and interestingly there was a fairly equal distribution of individuals using the drugs on a daily, weekly, monthly and yearly basis. One of the most frequently used drugs was Ritalin: we did a review to see if this was a prevalent practice and found data from the US describing how Ritalin was used on college campuses, suggesting that this involved between 3,7% and 11% of students – not something marginal (and we are talking here about self-reported behavior). How much of this really reflects reality is still unknown: I think we have poor prevalence data on the non-medical use of prescription drugs. In response to this situation, some neuroethics colleagues, Hank Greely from Stanford, John Harris from Manchester, and Martha Farah from Penn University, published a piece in *Nature* highlighting concerns with regard to cognitive enhancement. At this time, we do not have data on the non-medical uses of these types of drugs. There are many other concerns such as protecting the liberty of individuals to engage in those practices, and fair access – if the drugs were efficient, there would be an issue of ensuring fair access to them. Another issue is to gather more research-based evidence and, finally, to engage professional societies in proactive debate about the growing use of drugs and improving public understanding, while installing limited legislative action. This is what the authors of this Nature paper called for, and they highlighted these concerns while voicing the opinion that the proper social response is to be favorable to cognitive enhancement uses: they argued that cognitive enhancers should be viewed in the same general category as education, good health habits and information technology. I have no set idea of how we should conclude, necessarily; before concluding in favor of cognitive enhancers we need to seriously address the issues highlighted by the authors of this *Nature* piece. I will now show you some data that fleshes out the importance of those challenges and potentially their policy implications.

The first research we did was to examine how the media described cognitive enhancers. When you look at the terms used to describe cognitive enhancers, they do not look too scientific and you can sense the kind of expectations and belief they support. When we compared print media coverage to content from bioethics and public health, we found that they actually entertained fairly different views about this problem or issue.

In the print media, non-medical use of prescription drugs tended to be described as a lifestyle choice: the idea captured here is that we are more and more competitive and have access to different resources and, accordingly, neuropharmaceuticals are one of the ways that allow us to cope with growing pressures; consequently, non-medical use of prescription drugs is viewed as another lifestyle choice and individual decision. In bioethics there is a wide range of views on the term "cognitive enhancement" used in a way which may suggest that we can actually enhance [cognition], even though we have no good data to support this – which is problematic. If you look at public health discourse, you will actually find very negative labels attributed to this, such as "drug abuse" and "drug misuse". The perspectives (media, bioethics, public health) are therefore very different suggesting that various stakeholders have very different ethical opinions and beliefs. There have not been many debates about this, at least in my country.

I now want to highlight some of the gaps between the bioethics content and the print media: as you can see here, a lot of these issues are not discussed in the public domain or public health literature. There are a number of issues in particular that lead to a fair amount of debate, for example drug safety for non-medical use, considerations such as whether this constitutes cheating or not, the issue of justice and distributive justice, and, potentially, the lack of individual autonomy (coercion).

We looked at the potential recommendations put forth in different debates, and identified a range clearly showing that there is no consensus. In bioethics there are opinions ranging from the proposal to distribute these drugs to everybody right up to prohibition of non-medical uses: therefore the recommendations are diverse and scattered. We also examined if there were challenges related to the recommendations: in public health debates there does not seem to be a feeling that there will be obstacles in preventing or tackling those practices, which is really interesting. We are also seeing that where bioethics and media debates tend to be more optimistic the public health perspective tends to be negative, suggesting disengagement and a need for public health to look into the challenges of preventing or approaching the issue of cognitive enhancement.

The other piece of research I want to go through is based on focus groups, a method used in social science to examine opinions and reactions regarding a great range of topics, and in marketing research and policy studies to understand perspectives. We used focus groups to get a better idea of how stakeholders responded to ethical issues of cognitive enhancement: we recruited university students, their parents, and healthcare professionals, to focus on the non-medical use of Ritalin. We gained some insights with this research. One of them was the fact that these are prescription drugs, and they seem to convey a sense of safety to the students, but also to parents, that is, that they are safe in a general sense without taking into consideration the context in which they are used. They are safe, they said, otherwise physicians would not have prescribed them. What is interesting with focus groups is that they clearly show that students and citizens are clever and that there is a wide range of opinions in the public. For example, you see here that students clearly identify the problematic nature of a non-medical use of a prescription drug. If these practices are happening outside a supervised medical environment, adverse effects may not be reported, so the belief that there are no risks becomes a self-fulfilling prophecy because you have no reliable data on adverse effects.

Another important finding that we noted was that the way in which different stakeholders viewed this practice could suggest more widespread diversity in society at large: for example, non-medical uses have surfaced in the academia. Why would they not be used by medical professionals that perform in highly stressful environment, e.g. a neurosurgeon? This has actually been discussed in the peer review literature: what if you added the issue of making money, as one student suggested?

Another finding is that Ritalin was being considered as another type of resource, like drinking coffee and, interestingly, we found statements connected to this view suggesting that we identify these practices as the cause of problems. In fact, they may be a consequence of social pressure and expectation, rather than the cause. This would suggest that there are underlying forces shaping part of the context of cognitive enhancement.

The last piece of data I want to show to you is actually one of the most interesting we found. In a specifically Canadian context - and I would not know about this on an international level - we found that in a fairly broad sense stakeholders viewed the non-medical use of prescription drugs as within the purview of personal choice, and that it was considered an individual decision based on beliefs in personal liberty and respect for autonomy. I would counter-argue that this view is actually lip service to autonomy, and here is why: participants described this practice as the result of personal choice, but when we looked at [social] pressure they actually started describing huge social pressures to use these cognitive enhancers. These took the form of pressure to be best, competition with other students, changes in social expectations, and the fear of being at a disadvantage by not using cognitive enhancers. This led us to formulate the following model, where we suggest that there is a lip service to autonomy because the overwhelming social pressure that was described seemed to push strongly in favor of social acceptance without major criticism or review of the scientific aspect of this practice.

Now I am coming back to the *Nature* piece with a few comments based on the data I have presented to you, I think we have to be concerned with safety and we have to look seriously into this. We also have to look into public perceptions based on the data I showed you that suggest potential misunderstandings about the non-medical use of drugs like Ritalin: I think we have to be concerned with the issue of autonomy. It won't be straightforward to monitor and capture the different contexts in which, internationally speaking, cognitive enhancers will be used: if they are considered within a privileged academic environment, they can appear as a clear advantage in order to perform better. However, they may not be viewed in the same way in completely different contexts where demands are placed on individuals who are in a different kind of individual rights environment. Engagement of professional societies will need to be a priority, and we have not seen many medical societies being involved in debates. This will be one of the things to do in the future, but better public understanding is also an area of significant importance. What I fear with the emergence of the public debate on this, and its highly controversial aspects, is that legitimate use of medications like Ritalin will be viewed as an enhancement in itself: my fear is that some will over-generalize and the controversies about cognitive enhancement will overshadow this debate.

To conclude, I think that neuroethics and the neuroscience revolution point to a number of ethical responsibilities that need to be assumed. They need to be addressed by the scientific community in partnership with other stakeholders. These responsibilities range from ensuring integrity in the research environment to proactively tackling the ethical issues generated by neuroscience. For example, with regard to civic and democratic responsibility, my research shows that we need to move away from the idea that the media – and not only the media, but science popularization as a whole – is simply a pipeline. We need to reconsider our beliefs that scientific experts will just straightforwardly convey their message to the media: I think it is much more complicated than this. Science communication has to be based on a case-by-case approach, based on the types of technology and issues involved, and we also need to consider a more dynamic model of science communication where scientists try to engage in public discussion and public dialogue to explain the rationale behind their inquiry. Underlining this view, which we presented a few years ago in *Nature Reviews Neuroscience*, is the idea that science provides a model for public debate, because at its core is not only public discussion but a model based on some minimal commitments to reasonable public discourse. This way, science can provide a very interesting model for public debate. I want to thank my current and previous trainees who work with me and helped with this research. I also wish to acknowledge the different funding agencies without which this work would be impossible, as well as some of the international collaborators involved in the pieces of research I have presented today.

*Director, Neuroethics Research Unit,
Institut de recherches cliniques, Montréal, Canada

Freedom of research between funding,
careers and politics

Gabriela Gebrin Cezar*
**Freedom of scientific research as a vehicle
for social and economic transformation**

Thank you very much for the opportunity to participate in this seminal congress. It is an honor for me. I am actually a human embryonic stem cell scientist in the United States, at the University of Wisconsin-Madison. But today I am going to talk to you about a rather unorthodox topic for a human embryonic stem cell scientist, which is the role of freedom of scientific research in social and economic transformation.

I chose this topic due to a collection of facts that should provide a reasonable argument on how freedom of scientific research can indeed transform social and economic development. I will provide a few case studies today of situations where we have seen key developments, in two countries - in Brazil, where I am from, and in the United States. These case studies are a means to demonstrate that when we have a synchronized convergence and consolidated alliances between the government sector, the private sector and the academic bodies, we are actually able to generate and sustain a permissive environment for freedom of scientific research to ensue. More importantly in addition to long term perspectives, with the discovery of life saving therapies, for example, I propose that freedom of scientific research and its role in economic and social development is a shorter-term, immediate benefit of science in the lives of so many people. These benefits can be summarized, for example, as social and professional development of the individuals directly involved in the research, as well as benefits to the local economies and communities with the creation of high value, technical jobs and economic progress. For example, in the process of awaiting and developing potential therapies for neuro-developmental disorders, which is what we study in my laboratory, we are already transforming the lives of so many with the impact of science.

So what is the major driving point underlying the need for freedom of scientific research? Here is just some food for thought: we need to come up with new alternatives to feed, heal, fuel and clean the world. Where is the innovation going to come from? How are we

213

going to sustain innovation? How are new ideas going to arise to address this, to feed, heal, and clean the world? Freedom of scientific research is a major force to drive innovation and next generation solutions to many of our current challenges. In the absence of ethically guided freedom of scientific research, we cannot deliver on these challenges, such as medical needs that remain to be addressed.

I would also like to take this opportunity as a call to action to other scientists. Elena Cattaneo has talked about this aspect of our commitment in previous days. We really need to see a greater engagement from all of us, the scientists, in playing a transformative role in society in general, not just sitting inside the laboratories. We also need to participate especially in the economic process, the development of technologies and the integration of such technologies into society, whether in the form of new knowledge or new products that will benefit mankind. This is an area where there remain certain taboos among us scientists, when we talk about integrating science and economic development, since there are some of us who are in favor of public and private partnerships. On the other hand, scientists who pursue a more purist approach do not always welcome public-private partnerships as a positive alliance. The bottom-line to consider, at least for those of us involved in medical research is: how are we going to ultimately translate the science that we generate in our research laboratories into therapies for patients? Consider, for example, the many drugs that are currently taken, and the cures that we have available on the market, the infrastructure that is embedded in the development of therapies, and the exercise of technological development to take an idea to the bedside, all this requires alignment between academic or public sectors with private partners at some stage.

In my career I was faced with a very difficult decision in order to exercise my own freedom of scientific research. I had to leave the pharmaceutical industry, due to the fact that at that time we were not allowed to work on human embryonic stem cells. Things have changed in a significant manner since that decision, four years ago, and pharmaceutical companies have for the most part communicated public support of human embryonic stem cell research. Nonetheless, this was the most difficult decision of my career. Given the limitation to work on human embryonic stem cells, I left the industry and returned to academia and founded a laboratory. Our main research focus is to elucidate mechanisms that underlie human neuro-developmental disorders, such as fetal alcohol syndrome and autism. We take a very different approach to human embryonic stem cell research and how it is applied to help us answer some of these fundamental questions, and also how we view human embryonic stem cells as a resource to benefit patients in the future. Based on human embryonic stem cells, not therapies directly, we try to understand better ways to diagnose pediatric disorders. We actually take advantage of human embryonic stem cell technology and the ability of these cells to generate functional human brain cells to understand the mechanisms underlying neuro-developmental disorders and the causes of birth defects, many of which are preventable. About one in 33 children in the US is affected by a birth defect. The prevalence of birth defects is higher in lower-income countries, such as Brazil. That is really the underlying nature of our research. We focus on the ability of human embryonic stem cells to recapitulate human development to elucidate some of the molecular causes of birth defects and hopefully identify novel ways to diagnose and/or prevent such disorders.

Indeed, we have had the privilege to do this research, despite the challenging and difficult environment in the US – some of you must have heard about what it is like to be a stem cell scientist in the US for the past four to five years under the Bush administration. Under his policy, only 0,1% of the federal National Institutes of Health budget was allocated to human embryonic stem cell research. Our program, however, has been very, very fortunate to receive support from the NIH and we are very grateful for that and are doing our best to make critical progress in the field of fetal alcohol spectrum disorders with this research investment. The other disease we focus our research on is autism, where we developed an in vitro model based on human embryonic stem cell derived neural precursors and performed metabolomics. Based on what we learned with human embryonic stem cells, we were able to procure *post-mortem* brains from patients, from the Autism Tissue Program and are developing a global biochemical fingerprint for the autistic brain. Our research has taken us from an in vitro model to in vivo studies, and so far we have been able to identify small molecules whose abundance seems to be higher in the brains of autistic children compared to age-match controls. In the future, we might generate a chemical approach to diagnose autism. Currently, there is no chemical or biochemical alternative to diagnose autism, other than from behavioral changes. We also have a project that deserves particular mention due to the nature of Luca Coscioni's illness, where we developed an in-vitro model of Amyotrophic Lateral Sclerosis. We published this research in the journal *Cell Stem Cell* in December 2008, and it represents the delivery of a new model to discover new drugs for ALS.

So going back to the main topic, the role of freedom of scientific research on social and economic development. One of the reasons why I proposed this topic is due to the fact that I have played a direct role in the field of entrepreneurship. In my role as a scientist and an entrepreneur, I often have the opportunity to engage in activities at the Business School of our University, providing training for the next generation of entrepreneurs who have advanced degrees in science or medicine, but also working with government agencies at both federal and State levels to actually implement policy strategies that are going to be able to transform and translate science into products for patients and technology. Along the way you have to recognize that the freedom of scientific research can generate directly short-term benefits for so many people, prior to the delivery of the products we are talking about in medical research.

When we talk about benefits of stem cell research, these are the classic benefits: regenerative medicine, in vitro systems to discover new drugs or predict their toxicity to humans, and understanding how diseases evolve, or basic science. But if you think about it, ask yourself, what are the benefits of stem cells research today? We do have the first human embryonic stem cell-derived Food and Drug Administration clinical trial approved and in progress, with an indication for spinal cord injuries. However, while we have not fully delivered therapies, we are already delivering in vitro models of disease, such as the ALS example that I mentioned previously, and we are delivering new knowledge on basic science. So are there any direct benefits of stem cell research that we have already produced for society as whole? Yes, we have delivered benefits. I would propose that society has in fact actively benefited, not only patients, knowing that we are on the quest to find alternatives to treat their affections, but we have benefited people in so many different aspects of society. Give this some thought. We have benefited ourselves, at the level of the community of scientists. I definitely feel, as a scientist, that we are making a difference for the future of medicine. We are already benefiting people through the creation of jobs. This is one of the most important points of my speech - in that freedom of scientific research is a vehicle and a means to generate the next generation of job, especially in the face of economic crisis. Most importantly, another immediate, direct benefit that I see in freedom of scientific research that benefits society today is through the development of people. And this is something that really we had never thought about as scientists, even though these are stories that we see every day in hundreds of laboratories around the world. I have two amazing women as examples in my own laboratory, Alice and Jessica. Alice was my former laboratory manager. At 70+ years old, Alice would constantly be running around with books, and postponing her retirement for the opportunity to develop herself as a scientist and to be able to contribute in a new era of medicine. I truly believe this is one example of how our science is exerting direct benefits to development of talent, development of people, allowing them the freedom to pursue their individual growth. Jessica is another extraordinary woman with whom I had the honor of joining my team. Jessica grew up in rural Wisconsin and continues to pursue this lifestyle, managing a sheep farm and providing continuity to her family traditions, while at the same time, she is conducting cutting-edge, state-of-the-art stem cell research and is given the opportunity to present her work to the world, such as at meetings at the International Society of Stem Cell Research.

Let us talk about Brazil a little bit, the country where I am from. Brazil is an interesting example of how the freedom of scientific research has played a role in social transformation. The magazine, *Revista Epoca*, which has a weekly circulation of about half a million copies, had a cover story about the status of stem cell research. One of the reasons my work was featured in it was because I was commenting on the debate that lasted for years in the Supreme Court in Brazil to allow the use of human embryonic stem cells in research. The article also told the story of why scientists like myself are finding opportunities and permissive environments in other countries. Brazil is the largest Catholic country in the world, with approximately 150 million Catholics, and yet, finally, human embryonic stem cell research is approved there, as long as the discarded embryos that are used in the research have been stored for three years or more. We finally were able to circumvent the challenges.

While Brazil has faced limitations with human embryonic stem cell research, with policies and regulations still being fully implemented for stem cell research, it is in several aspects a nation in development. It is another example of how freedom of scientific research leads to social transformation as well. Brazil is a global leader and occupies center stage in the global progress of regenerative medicine. Two of the top clinical trials in stem cells, published in prestigious journal such as JAMA - *The Journal of the American Medical Association and Circulation Research*, were initiated and executed in Brazil, with the support of its Ministry of Health. One of these clinical trials, for heart disease, is actually going to involve 1,200 patients, and is also supported and funded by the Brazilian Ministry of Health. Here again science is transforming society and its development, in a country that has not yet reached a comparable funding environment for innovation to highly developed nations, it still achieves center stage in terms of scientific accomplishment. Another amazing aspect of Brazilian progress in stem cell technology is given by an entity called National Network for Stem Cell Therapy. I have not seen in any of the countries that I have worked in, either in the United States, or in Europe, a similar infrastructure that is so organized for the delivery of stem cell therapies to patients such as this network. It has 42 accredited hospitals working seamlessly. I have communicated to the National Secretary of Health, Reinaldo Guimaraes, who unfortunately could not join us today, that what they have implemented in Brazil should be publicly and globally available as an example for other nations.

So, going back to some of the economic development aspects of freedom of scientific research, I will give a case study of where we are in the State in which I live, Wisconsin. Wisconsin ranks as the 19th State in the United States, in terms of economic contribution to the country. We are primarily a State focused on agriculture and manufacturing, the latter suffering from a relatively steady decline in jobs, as many regions in Europe. Nonetheless, Wisconsin has this critical alignment between the government, the private sector and the academic bodies that has guaranteed a permissive environment for scientific research to progress.

Our ability to conduct human embryonic stem cell research, for example, has been threatened since the state of Wisconsin elected a Republican assembly and senate. However, our (Democratic) governor, Jim Doyle, has said: "I have my veto pen and I will veto any initiative coming from the State legislature to block human embryonic stem cell research". He played a critical role in assuring that we would be able to continue to pursue this research in the State, since it was banned in other States in the US, such as Michigan and Louisiana. This demonstrates, once more, how science should also remain engaged with the political process to sustain freedom of scientific research. Wisconsin was in fact chosen as the location for the NIH National Stem Cell Bank. So, all the human embryonic stem cell lines approved to receive federal funding that one orders, are being archived, characterized and distributed from Wisconsin to the world. In Wisconsin, we have the private sector working in alignment with the government institutions for economic development and support from the federal government.

As the 19th state in the US economy, we contribute about 1,8% of the GDP of the country. Biotechnology alone, however, generates nine billion dollars per year in revenue for the State and 38,000 jobs for Wisconsin, as the Wisconsin Technology Council has recently reported. University of Wisconsin-Madison is the third institution in the US for receipt of research dollars, and we have used those dollars not only to generate knowledge, but also to transform and improve our community. We have a permissive political environment, private sector support, and transparency. This is another important advantage I see in the structure of our society. We have transparency. I am a scientist and entrepreneur. I am a founder of a company in Wisconsin, as is Dr. Jamie Thompson, the scientist who discovered human embryonic stem cells. We have support and transparency and vehicles in place to address and manage conflicting issues. As a result of this integration among all the different sectors, we have made an impact on the local economy. I would like you to take this example home and try to exercise and expand this model to other segments, particularly other countries here in Europe. You and I have heard for the past three days here a call to action from this institution, the European Parliament, from the European Commission, a call to action to build the next generation of job opportunities. We have also heard about brain drain in science and technology, and we know what is going on in some of the more traditional industries, such as manufacturing in the US and in Europe. We need to allow science and innovation to have a transformative role in economic development.

One of the last points I would like to make, or rather, the take-home message is this: a call for the alignment among the government, the private sector and the academic bodies. We, the scientists, need to become more interested and involved in politics. We, the scientists, need to become more interested and involved in economic development and we should also be open to interaction with the private sector.

I would also like to summarize the key points that should be in effect and in place in order to fully exercise freedom of scientific research as a vehicle for social transformation and economic transformation. First and foremost: people. Retaining talent, developing talent. Talent from students and young scientists that needs to be fostered and developed and given the freedom to innovate and remain alive, under strict ethical standards, of course. We need to recognize the fact that science knows no borders. Global competitiveness is in effect in terms of science and business. We now have VIPCOs - Virtually Integrated Pharmaceutical Companies, where parts of companies are operating in synergy in China, Brazil, and the US. We must create conditions locally to compete globally, and we have to recognize that we need exposure to investment opportunities and capital. It is so, in my point of view, critical to sustain and enable science through all of these aspects that we have discussed in order to benefit patients and society in general and bring about sustainable economic development.

*Assistant Professor,
University of Wisconsin-Madison, USA

Piergiorgio Strata*
The investment for research and innovation in Italy

Given the title of this session, I would like to make some general considerations in connection to the speech by Philippe Busquin, former Commissioner for European Research. I start from a *Green Paper* published by the European Commission in April 2007. We have to consider that a number of Asiatic countries are emerging by investing a great deal in research so that the Asian continent occupies now the first position among the various continents.

The European Council in Lisbon in March 2000 approved the proposal to create an European Research Area for a Knowledge Society, a basic prerequisite for economical development. There was a commitment to develop research, education, learning and innovation. The agreement in Lisbon was to lift up the investment from 1,8% of the GDP to a value of 3% in order to match the USA and Japan. However, we are still below 2%. At the same time private investment, which in Europe was at a ratio of 1:1 relative to the public sector, should have raised to 2:1 as in the USA. The private capital invested in research migrates heavily from Europe towards USA and it is poor in the opposite direction.

The principal obstacles in developing a research area in Europe are due to the fragmentation of programs and infrastructures and to the scarce mobility of the scientists, as opposed to the high mobility in the USA. The latter factor, which is essential for science development, is hampered, among others, by the heterogeneity of labour contract legislation for young investigators in different European countries. But also differences with USA and Asiatic countries create problems. An agreement, at least at the European level, seems a most urgent issue.

What is the position of Italy in this context? The investment in research is around 1% of the GDP with a minor contribution from the private sector. Fragmentation of initiatives and infrastructures is most dramatic. The capacity to attract international resources has diminished considerably. In the last ten years the ratio between what Italy is paying to Europe and what comes back changed from 14/11 to 15/9. Instructive are the data taken from the most prestigious international programme in life sciences, the Human Frontier Science Program. In the last five years Italy has assisted to a progressive reduction of its return in a ratio of 3,6 to 1. The main deficiency is the capacity to attract foreign investigators. Recent data show that out of almost 700 applicants for a postdoctoral fellowship to be spent in a foreign country of their choice, less than 1% of them asked to work in Italy. These data are confirmed by the results of the young investigators program recently launched by the European Research Council. Italy saw a good performance in applications and allocation of grants, but failed in the number of those who have come to work in Italy.

These data bring to mind the program to counter the brain drain, an European problem that is most dramatic in Italy. Philippe Busquin said yesterday that in Europe there is a lack of researchers. He said that in order to come to a balance between the European continent and the others, we need to find 800,000 researchers. Brains now move, like capitals, from countries to countries. Scientists not only search for good salaries, but also for infrastructures where they may do competitive work, and they migrate to those countries where they can find opportunities to compete. We need to make Europe competitive at this important level.

As far as Italy is concerned, programs that fund salaries to Italians who aim at coming back are fine. However, I hope that my country, Italy, will be capable of understanding that to attract brains, it is not enough to give out money. This is just a sort of treason. We need to create infrastructures. We need to have a good cause. We need to have Ferrari racing cars in infrastructures. The Italians can win that way.

*Scientific Director,
European Brain Research Institute;
Co-President, Luca Coscioni Association

Martin L. Perl*
**Limitations on research and development
in science and technology**

It is a wonderful pleasure and an honor to be here. I come out of
different worlds, the academic world of research in physics and engineering and the technology world of Silicon Valley. I will talk about
the economic-political limitations on R&D (research and development) and how we can find the money to do more of the right kind
of research and development. The OECD (Organization for Economic Co-operation and Development) definition of R&D is "creative work undertaken on a systematic basis in order to increase the
stock of knowledge, including knowledge of mankind, culture and
society, and the use of this stock of knowledge to devise new application".

The world's economic future is always uncertain and particularly
so at present. I will try to average over the uncertainty considering
the period 2000 to 2009. And I am going to use approximate numbers, doing what we call in physics back-of-the-envelope calcula-
tions, 20-40% approximations are fine. I do not account for inflation
or the subtleties in currency differences. All monetary amounts are
in US dollars.

I consider research and development funding together, recognizing that it is impossible to cleanly separate the two activities. One
hundred years ago development, including invention, was primary
and research secondary. Today research has grown in importance
although development funding is still the largest.

The total amount of the world's R&D expenditures is about 1,000
billion US$ with 2/3 spent on development. The US spends the most,
about 1/3 of the total, which is 280 billion US$. The other leaders are:
EU-25 about 210 billion US$, Japan about 120 billion US$ and China
about 80 billion US$.

The ratio of total R&D expenditures to the GDP for a country or region is historically and politically important. In descending order
this ratio is largest for Japan, United States, Germany, France, United
Kingdom, and Canada, ranging between 3% and 2%. So the ratio of
total R&D to GDP is of the order of a few percent in the countries

with the best funding. We would dearly like to increase this ratio, for example we would like to triple or quadruple it. History is against such a dream. Doubling funding in some R&D sectors has often been promised but rarely accomplished. Engineers and scientists must come to terms with the total amount of public and private monies that are available for R&D.

R&D expenditures are either government funded or privately funded, the latter consisting of both commercial and philanthropic funding. In our democracies we can do little directly and immediately about the nature and distribution of private funding for R&D, although it is very important. We have to transform the nature and distribution by discussion and persuasion. But in our democracies we can act directly on public funding and the remainder of this paper is concerned with public funding of R&D (the data in this section is taken from *The US National Science Foundation, Science and Engineering Indicators* 2006).

Military R&D expenditures are a big part of publically funded R&D. The major spending is by the United States, China, Russia, and some European countries.

My discussion is limited to the United States. But this same discussion applies to all nations with substantial military establishments. I am not a pacifist; I believe that nations have the right of active and efficient self-defense and the right to protect their borders and peoples. But I also believe that military R&D expenditures can be substantially reduced.

The largest items in the proposed United States Federal R&D budget are:

- Defense Budget - 100 billion US$ including weapons funding from the Department of Energy and other items
- National Institutes of Health - 30 billion US$, may be larger because of stimulus funding
- NASA - 17 billion US$
- Department of Energy (non-defense) - 6 billion US$, may be larger because of stimulus funding.

So the total United States R&D budget is 150 to 160 billion US$ with about 100 billion going into military R&D. I suspect the relative numbers are about the same in China and Russia, but less in European countries.

I will give two examples of how the United States can reduce the amount of its military R&D: the Future Combat Systems R&D and the Joint Strike Fighter R&D. Similar examples hold for other countries. My information comes from the press and executive branch and congressional branch published reports.

The Future Combat Systems is an R&D program costing about 4 billion US$ per year. This is a sensor, information transmittal system, and intelligence system that propose under battlefield conditions to connect dozens of military vehicles and units: airplanes, submarines, ships, command units, and in-the-field units. It proposes to modernize modern warfare.

I believe this proposal is unrealistic. Those of us who have worked on large computer and sensor systems know how difficult it is to build a totally reliable hardware and software system. There are many problems: bugs in the software, hardware instabilities, the need for backward compatibility, the security requirement, and the need for speed.

I am involved in building a large telescope in Chile for which we have to gather data and correct it, so professional and amateur astronomers can use it openly. It has to be right and it has to be backward compatible. This is a tremendous software task that we can only accomplish under peaceful and stable conditions.

The Future Combat Systems will be many times more difficult to build compared to our telescope data handling system, the programs are much more complicated because they must handle many types of data, and the hardware must work under battlefield conditions and must be protected against attack. In peacetime the Future Combat Systems will be very easy to hack. Bright teenagers will be able to do so once they break through computer security barriers.

If the Future Combat Systems is ever built, it will cost more than 100 billion US$. Recently US Secretary of Defense Gates has suggested the program be ended.

It will be much harder to abandon the Joint Strike Fighter R&D program that is developing the designated F-35. There are two arguments for the Joint Strike Fighter. The first argument is that a new concept and new technology will enable the Air Force, the Navy and the Marines to use the same general design leading to an economy of scale. The second argument has to do with the fleet of almost two hundred advanced United States Air Force airplanes called F-22s. The F-22 is expensive, about 150 million US$, and has never been used in combat. The United States Congress is prepared to have the F-22 eventually replaced by the F-35, which might be cheaper.

There are manifold objections to the F-35 Joint Strike Fighter concept. First the military forces have different requirements: for the Navy, the plane has to get on and off an aircraft carrier; for the Air Force, extensive electronic equipment is desired; and for the Marines, close support for landings and combat is required. The economy of scale argument may be mostly false. A second objection is that it is possible to upgrade existing airplanes to do the same tasks. A third objection is production cost. A few prototypes have been built but the estimated production cost per plane is 150 million US$, the same as the F-22, and may be larger. The proposal is to build 2,000 planes, an expense of 300 billion US$.

Our annual R&D expenditure for the Joint Strike Fighter is over 6 billion US$. The political problem, of stopping the Joint Strike Fighter program is overwhelming; Joint Strike Fighter contractors will exist in almost every State of the replacing F-22 contractors.

By switching some military R&D into non-defense R&D, we could gain substantial sums and not harm defense at all. Does that mean there should be no military R&D? No. For example, if we could develop an open system for detection of short-range missiles, a system to detect them and shoot them down, that would be a great step in world peace. It has to be an open system. Everybody would have to be able to use it. We have had such systems in the past but they have not worked. For example the Patriot system did not defend Israel against SCUD missiles.

Substantial public R&D funds are wasted in what I call grandiose scientific and engineering projects. I have three examples:
- the International Space Station
- programs to develop economically feasible controlled fusion devices for producing electric power
- proposals to send humans to the moon again and then to Mars.

The International Space Station is a grand science fiction idea come to reality; it is fun to learn about and to learn how it works (well, it sort of works). But the fun has not been worth the more than 100 billion US$ or greater cost. First, nothing of basic consequence has been learned in physics or chemistry and some experiments have never been installed. Second, the space station was supposed to be zero gravity but it vibrates leading to random small accelerations that are equivalent to small gravitational forces. Third, some has been learned about human physiology but not 100 billion US$ worth. Fourth, there has been considerable space engineering experience, but most of it is useless.

After all this, we do not have a modern, reliable way to get people up to the station and back to Earth. And once we discontinue the Space Shuttle we have to use the Russian Soyuz landing system. Soyuz uses a parachute and retro-rockets on landing. It is a rough but reliable landing system. It is a 40-year old system that has been improving steadily. And the whole world depends on it now. So, three cheers for the Russians. Old technology is not necessarily bad;

one can improve it slowly step after step. The International Space Station has been a waste of money.

Since the 1960s the physics and energy worlds have hoped to develop and build electric power plants using the controlled fusion of deuterium and tritium nuclei. Unfortunately a very complicated process is required to get deuterium and tritium to collide and fuse. And this process must produce more energy than is used. So far controlled net production of energy has not been achieved.

There are two paths towards controlled fusion. One process called thermonuclear controlled fusion uses a very hot gas inside a container with magnetic fields keeping the hot deuterium and tritium nuclei away from the colder walls. There is an international proposal to build an ITER (International Thermonuclear Experimental Reactor) in France with much of the major engineering test work in Japan. This sort of splitting is not a good idea in very large projects, but it was required by international concerns. There are doubts as to the success of this facility and a yet larger one may have to be built. The present estimated cost is 10 billion euros. My analysis predicts a cost increase of at least 50% and a completion after 2020.

There is another plan in the United States for obtaining controlled fusion by using hundreds of lasers to ignite a small capsule containing deuterium and tritium, laser-induced fusion. It would be a very small hydrogen bomb, not dangerous. By exploding many pellets per second the heat would be used to produce electric power. This United States project is called NIF (the National Ignition Facility) and so far it costs 4 billion US$. A similar project called LMU is being built in France.

Charles Seife's book *Sun in a Bottle* is a good summary of the history and future of thermonuclear controlled fusion and laser induced fusion. Seife is pessimistic about the success of either path and I too am pessimistic.

My third example of a grandiose project is the proposal to again send humans to the moon and then to Mars. In the United States this would be a NASA led project. NASA has been successful in the early days of getting human space travel going. It has worked very well. At the same time, things not run by people have worked better such as the Hubble telescope and many European space projects. Also, large Earth-based optical and radio telescopes have been operated by European, Japanese, and United States astronomers with great success.

Returning to the Moon will cost 100 billion US$. And going to Mars will cost much more. Plus the Moon to Mars trip involves the unsolved problem of excess exposure to radiation.

Indications of grandiosity are:
- basic science may be sketchy;
- substantial underestimation of costs;
- premature or uneconomical engineering and design;
- over publicized;
- exorbitant promises;
- aggrandizement of some government departments;
- may be military connections.

A final example is the commercial supersonic transport. This project was killed in the United States, but Europe could not resist the grandiosity pressures. The expense of the R&D, of the production of the 14 flight-ready Concordes, and of the operation overwhelmed the project. The total cost was over 20 billion US$. D. R. Myddelton's book *They Meant Well: Government Project Disasters* is an excellent summary.

The limitation on monies available for basic research will be mitigated by ending grandiose scientific and engineering projects that cost a great deal but produce little or no benefits to humanity.

National specialization in R&D enables more inventive and original R&D:
- build on national R&D strengths;
- avoid the "not-invented-here" prejudice;
- do not compete just because of national pride;
- be willing to use the fruits of the R&D of others.

I will give a few examples. The United States is preeminent in many areas of biology and medicine and we should continue to strongly support R&D in these areas. NASA has been very successful in unmanned space research and should continue this research. But NASA should get out of the development and building of manned space vehicles. We should leave this R&D to Russia, China and India.

As a final example the United States should get out of the automotive R&D business. The Japanese and Germans are doing very well in automobiles and batteries. There is nothing wrong with copying from them or partnering with them. This is my advice.

*Nobel Prize in Physics, 1995

Josè Mariano Gago*
Science, technology and scientific education in Portugal

Thank you very much for your invitation and for pursuing this initiative of creating a forum to discuss this difficult subject. It is difficult to be sensible on these matters. You have framed it as freedom of research. I will take that as a starting point. For ten years now I have been a Minister of Science and Technology. I am also a physicist. I have spent almost all my life at it. So, I would like to contribute to the discussion through reflections regarding problems concerning freedom of research that I have had to face myself, also during my government activity.

Of course, one of the most difficult problems in the European Union is represented by freedom to do research on stem cells. This is one of the points that we all have in common. That is the issue. The debate and the contributions today are mostly related to this issue and mainly focus on religion and organizations acting against the freedom of research. This is somehow not new. It is a very old thing but renewed with very specific characteristics. Politically, it is not simple. You cannot say that you have on the one hand the scientists and on the other the right-wing parties. Why did the German Social Democrats encounter difficulties in that debate? This did not happen only to the Right in Italy. It has mainly to do with history, namely with the history of Germany during the 20th century.

Things are not as simple as that. I will expose other problems concerning freedom of research. I am not going to put them in order. In non-democratic countries for sure, even in countries where very large investments are made in science, research is certainly not free in some areas like history and social sciences. In these areas free research is typically not allowed, although huge sums are invested in physics, chemistry and others. Trying to protect and to help the scientists and the students there represents a problem of science policy for democratic countries. Should you collaborate with these countries, please insist that you do not accept their own terms. Their historians must be granted the freedom to travel freely, publish freely and so on.

Basic science also represents a difficult area as far as it concerns freedom of research in our own countries. Basic science should be used as a tool of critique. Very large technology and industrial projects of public interest claim to be pursued in spite of any type of critique. But they are probably not that grandiose, on the contrary they are probably just industrial projects that have only counted upon large sums of money for many years. They do not care for any care of critique, they are not basic-science oriented and want to be protected from critiques based on it.

Recently the freedom of the internet has also been discussed about. That means a great deal to us. The debate is a very confused one. The internet organization is almost unique in the world. In fact it is neither governed by multi-lateral agreements nor by a United Nations or telecommunication union agreement. Multiple stakeholders govern it, including scientists, industry, and governments. But according to some, a tax against this state of affairs is getting to be more and more important every year. They have good press coverage, because they present themselves as being anti-American and trying to fight the monopoly of United States in that sense. It is very stupid because, of course in my view, if a body of bureaucrats appointed by the United Nations governed the internet, it would be a complete disaster. What I am saying is certainly not politically correct. If we want to keep the internet free, as free as it is now, we must try to protect this kind of multi-stakeholders organization that has miraculously survived until now.

There are two specific issues I would like to highlight. One is the relation between scientific freedom and its risks; the other is the research integrity which is recently very much in discussion. I am deeply concerned with freedom of scientific research in these areas. As for the risks, I will tackle for instance nanotechnology. The recent concern about nano-risks pushes nowadays towards their regulation and to a legal framework, which would be extremely damaging for any type of scientific research. This is the way populists act. It is very easy to sell risks and to sell fear to people. It is very easy to get votes from people who are just afraid. The new frontier I see at least in the European Union is an attempt by traditional environmental groups to convince others that nano is a devil to be controlled as much as possible. If you have to shift your attention from the issue of stem cells to another, I suggest that the next field will be nano. It has not the ingredients of stem cells, namely the impact on the traditional view of life that stem cells have, hence it will not produce the same uproar. Nano-medicine will. And the relationship between nano-technologies and molecular biology will certainly produce the same effects as stem cells. A very dangerous movement is emerging and should be counteracted as soon as possible.

The second issue at stake is research integrity. We are all in favor of it. Of course nobody wants scientists to lie and fake results. This does not happen very often because research is not an isolated activity; on the contrary it is a collective, social one. When science is free and published and discussed about, that creates the social and human environment that will not encourage such behavior. This has been known for a long time as it emerged in the 17th and 18th Century in the United Kingdom. That is part of our scientific life now. Research integrity is concerned with it. When there is a danger, integrity must be assured. The traditional response to this concern is: to help research integrity you must help the integrity of research institutions. You must protect the integrity of universities and of public research programs from being subject to undue influence of other sources, be they military, religious, economic and so on. That is the traditional democratic way of addressing the issue of research integrity, not focusing on the individuals but on the institutions. From a point of view of science policy, what the legislator should do to protect integrity to help the institutions. In recent years the attention has been shifted from the integrity of institutions to the personal integrity. Some people in the United States and elsewhere have been actively promoting the idea that gatekeepers of research integrity should be inside each laboratory, making independent reports to the funding authorities, a sort of lawyerly inquisition making sure that individuals there behave properly. It seems funny, but it is not funny at all. That is a very strong movement nowadays. Many Asian countries are looking very carefully at it. They are trying to actively pursue that approach.

The issue of research integrity must be seen and must be followed very carefully in my opinion. If I had to choose two threads, I would choose risks and the relation between risks and science. Of course we need scientists to come into the game of the discussion on sensible risk governance and try to protect the public opinion and policy-makers from the populist view. If someone says that there is a big risk, you all, Ministers and Parliamentarians, will be responsible. Are you going to address this issue or not, then? You must say: "Well, there is no risk there". In order to do this, you need a stronger involvement of the scientists themselves in public life, namely in issues concerning risk governance. In the future, nano-risks will probably be one of the most crucial issues along with research integrity.

My last point is a much simpler one: it is about the possibility of young people to engage in research and in science. In some developed countries, not all, the real problem still concerns women and women's freedom to engage in science. This is a frontier for growth for all of us and very difficult to cross in some countries where there is a very strong cultural and political resistance against women's engagement in full-time work, especially when they are highly educated. In some countries, it is much easier to accept a woman without education to be a full-time worker, than to accept a highly educated woman to become a professional scientist. Of course, if schools are not open after two o'clock in the afternoon, things are certainly not very simple. The relation between science policy and social policy is still a hidden area for freedom of research for a large part of the population in many countries. I think you are right in addressing the issue of stem cells, the issue of life research as a matter of priority. Even these matters of research integrity and the nano will converge into life sciences, because there you can maximize the combinations of the enemies of scientific freedom, such as economic, military interests and religious organizations. I think you are right in addressing that issue as a matter of priority. Thank you very much.

Marco Perduca (*Italian Senator and chairman of the session*):
We thank you very much, Minister Gago. I think many of us that are involved in politics would have never imagined that one day in the early years of 2000, Italy would have to look at Spain and Portugal for avantgarde technologies and liberal laws. We envy your young democracy that has been able to go in the right direction. Italy is going at the opposite of what you are doing.

Minister Gago: It is the result of having 50 years of fascism in our country.

M.P.: You have learnt the lesson. We had 20 years of fascism and 60 years of partitocracy and I am not seeing any kind of reaction against that. I am sure it is what has guided you. Your new priorities will be taken into consideration. We do not have a minister of science and technology, but nobody in the political spectrum has spoken about nanotechnology so far. If nobody knows about technology, all the risks and all they want to impose, they can do whatever they want. In silence they can go on. What is scarier is the creation of mini Soviets in research lab. I would like to take this opportunity to transform it into a question time. You mentioned at the beginning the fact that the zealots, be they secular or religious, were those that posed possibly greater problems in terms of pressure to adopt a legislation that would, under this banner of being concerned with the risks, impose limitations on science research. What was the experience in Portugal? And mainly, how could you actually effectively counter those that we consider assaults on freedom? One of the slogans that we used to convene the first session of the congress in Rome three years ago was to counter obscurantism and fundamentalism. I do not know if we have been able to do it at home because again we have a center-right government, opposing anything that has to do with freedom. And you said, it is not a left or right issue. It is completely true, zealots and fundamentalists are on both sides of the aisle. They belong to all parties. My question was: how were you able, not only politically, but as society?

Minister Gago: Very interesting question. I can answer from my personal experience. This has been addressed differently in many countries and situations. First, I think that you are right: there is not a specific distribution of bigotry and zealotry across the spectrum, but on average it tends to concentrate on the extreme right-hand side of the political spectrum, no doubt. In Portugal what has been part of the scientific debate in the last decade is that from a social point of view, you cannot have scientific development, and you cannot protect scientific freedom, if you do not make large investments in the scientific culture of the population at large. That requires the promotion of a culture of proximity, of personal proximity between scientists and non-scientists. To see a scientist on the screen is not enough. The opportunity of direct personal interactions between scientists and non-scientists across the country should be increased. That happened at the beginning of the movement started more than ten years ago, *Ciencia viva*, generously involving some hundreds of scientists. We have been having twinning of schools and research institutions. Every summer, we have science courses in biology, geology and so on, where hundreds of scientists generously spend time of their holidays in various activities with the public. It is part of the popular holidays in our own country. Moreover we have created quite a large network of science centers, where you can expect to find scientists, and people go there and address scientists on some topics that have nothing to do with their knowledge but with their kids' education and the information they want to get about health or something else. The human social barriers are sobroken. The idea of creating as much as possible within the scientific community a movement towards the general public and within the general public a culture of proximity with scientists, namely at schools, has been for us a very important measure. It has then developed into a non-governmental organization that is of course supported by the State, but it has also become a popular movement for science, which helped enormously when difficulties came. When stem cells were at stake, there was almost no discussion. In the public spirit, that represented no problem at all. Of course in the parliament there was a debate. The zealots did try to draw the public opinion to their cause but the very first day they knew it was lost. The real people, the general public wanted to listen to the scientists they knew and to the science they knew, that had been with them for quite a long time. They were not newcomers. I think this type of cultural proximity, by networking scientists and non-scientists on non-formal basis, connecting scientific organizations with schools, science centers and others, creating direct lines through the internet and other means, so that non-scientists may pose questions to scientists, is part of our social responsibility. And I think we cannot have scientific freedom without some type of scientific responsibility.

M.P.: Thank you very much. Last question would be: the role of the media in all this?

Minister Gago: Frankly I have doubts about it. Ten years ago it changed dramatically. It has to do with the evolution of the media industry and the fact that the competition for advertisement contracts has been extremely fierce in the last few years. I would say that ten years ago it was much easier; the media in general were extremely supportive of this type of movement for scientific culture then. Now they are not actually against it, but it is not part of their agenda anymore. They do not feel it sells. What really sells now is blood. Blood and crime sell enormously along with political maneuvering, because it is a kind of soccer game played by politicians. Scientists are right, but who cares? I would say that this is the tendency, but frankly I may be wrong. I would suggest that scientists' organizations and civic organizations that are related to these areas need to be their own media and have their own media. Moreover, if I had to consider new priorities in terms of science budgets and science policy, I would suggest that you need to devote much more funds to the budget for science, just to do what the media used to do ten years ago, that is to inform people. They do not inform people now. You have to inform them. Of course they will, if you pay them for advertisement space. By example, ten years ago, science news could not take but two to three minutes for something important during prime time in TV. Now it is extremely difficult, except when there is a drama. If there is no drama and you really want to inform people, what you have to do is to buy some advertising space. If you do that and if you pay,

WORLD CONGRESS FOR FREEDOM OF SCIENTIFIC RESEARCH

people will get news. I think that is in the interest of the public to do that. I think that you should carefully consider that part of the budget should be devoted to that. Thank you.

*Minister for Science and Technology,
Portugal

The way ahead:
the global monitoring on the state
of freedom of research and other missions
for a permanent World Congress

Andrea Boggio*
**Freedom of research around the globe:
a preliminary study**

The project I am presenting today is ambitious and interesting. The organization has been excellent, spot-on.

Today, I will talk about a project on monitoring the freedom of research. I will talk about my role and the fact I conducted a pilot study - that is the part of the research process in which the methodology is tested. A word of caution: it is work in progress, so take the findings with a grain of salt, because they are not conclusive. I will show what we are doing.

The aim of the project is to monitor from a global perspective the state of affair of medical research and practice. We really do more than just monitor research: it includes medical practice. I framed it in this way and I will defend later the notion that the practice of medicine is important in understanding what nations are doing. In fact, the project focuses on biomedical advances more generally.

The project is global. I worked with Alex Mauron in Geneva on a project that had a similar aim. It is a complicated task, to say anything about its precision. It raises a lot of challenges when one tries to narrow down what the differences are and what is that determines such differences. Nonetheless, it is exciting and it will be an important contribution to the international debate.

To some extent, the model of project is the *Freedom of the Press report* published by Freedom House in Washington, DC, which has been monitoring the freedom of press for many years now. That is our ultimate goal as well, but we are not there yet.

One of the challenges of the project is to talk meaningfully about freedom and what we mean by it. One of the easy things here to do is that I do not have to persuade this audience that freedom is relevant and important. That is not an issue here. But what do we mean by freedom? I am an academic, and therefore, my contribution is not really the political contribution. It is to develop a contribution from theoretical perspective. But it is true that academics - it has been done and proposed here - must take an active role in thinking about policy and in contributing as professionals in the field. This is my professional contribution: shaping up the study from a theoretical and methodological perspective. As academics, our tools and weapons to shape policy are theory and methodology. Then you can propose empirical findings. That is the motivation.

So, the talk will mirror what I think my contribution to policy is. I will talk about theory, methodology, findings and the future of this project in the event you have the curiosity of being involved in some capacity.

What is freedom? Freedom is a controversial concept. I teach a class in political philosophy that runs for 15 weeks. We spend 45 hours in class and we do not get to an ultimate conclusion of what we mean by freedom. It is a controversial concept. Some of the theoretical perspectives were discussed at this conference. One of the papers discussed the various approaches to freedom from political perspective. It means different things to different people. Some adopt a narrow vision - for instance, the American vision is a narrow one - and some a more positive one - where the government has an obligation to do something for individuals. This is politically very controversial. I propose, and I use, a non-controversial version of freedom, one that is deprived of its politically charged meanings, and one that allows to achieve the purpose of the study, that is to say to measure freedom. Economists talk about "operationalizing" a concept when they try to find ways of empirically measuring concepts. Here, I will try to pinpoint aspects of freedom we can measure so that we can then put together the report.

What is important to me is that freedom is a matter of degree. We are trying to measure the degrees that separate non-freedom from complete freedom. Intuitively, there is a lot of variation in between, and I could provide an illustration. If I was in the audience, I would be more free: I could go out, make phone calls. On the other hand, while I am here giving a talk, I cannot do it. I have an obligation to talk and look at you. We are both free from a political perspective, but the conditions are different and I can say that I am less free than you are. Professor Perl is the only presenter with a shirt. Maybe the Nobel Prize status allows him to wear a shirt instead of a suit. That is the kind of problems we are facing. Freedom is a matter of degree, and there are ways to measure it.

Although freedom is a very complicated question, I purposely use a very simple yet persuasive definition of freedom borrowed from Gerald McCallum. McCallum sees freedom as a triadic relation among three elements. The elements are 1) an actor, 2) conducting an action, 3) under certain conditions. Actions and actor are positive. But conditions are what we cannot do because of procedures or rules or other reasons. That is where we have to focus our attention as researchers. That is where we find divergence. We can measure how different actors and environments can undertake different actions. The definition of freedom is so a triadic relation between three things: preventing conditions affecting actions of an agent.

In our case, the actors are the researchers or the medical practitioners, the action is performing research or practicing medicine, and the conditions are those set by the legal environment, law being one of the restraints imposed on people. I will expand this notion later. In sum, focusing on the conditions is an easy way of measuring freedom.

Who are the actors? The first day we discussed whether basic fundamental research and applications ought to be studied separately. That is not what we do here. I will try to make a defense why these two groups must be together. The idea is the following: there is continuum between what fundamental research is and developing applications, which moves from research to treating patients. These are different steps done by different people, often with conflicting interests. Yet there is in a continuum. We go from A to Z and you cannot have one without the other steps. So, they are all together in a same conceptual frame. In fact, what brings them together is the idea that at the end of the day, the justification for doing that, for spending that money, for thinking about it, is the well-being of individuals. I want to stress the idea that my notion of individuals is more like a citizen. Yet, it is about individuals' well-being.

What is the connection between well-being and research? One justification is provided by Amartya Sen when he argues that development, human and economic development, the idea of well-being, is linked to freedom, and in particular, the proposition that development and growth are about expanding freedom. You cannot have development and well-being without freedom. Why? Because if you are free, you can make better choices affecting your development, you can shape the life around your own desires as stressed by liberal thinking and social-oriented thinking. That is what we aim at: to see freedom as serving the ultimate good for humans.

What are the conditions and what do we measure? How are we going to measure that? To operationalize this notion and have data, in collaboration with Marco and others, I focused on a limited number of controversial areas because this is a pilot and because of the limited resources in time. I focused on four areas. Most of the data collection was done by students under my direction, and I want to acknowledge in particular the contribution of Joseph Robertson.

For each area, I listed some questions that are relevant to measure, in a certain context, what researchers can do. I assigned a score to each of the questions, and the points depend upon the answers. The score is very low, where you have complete freedom, a zero. If you are completely prevented from doing something, then you have five points, which is the maximum available. And the degrees of freedom are distributed on a scale between 0 and 5. At the end, you sum up the points and the result is a number representing freedom for each of the areas. Then, what I did is to allocate 25 points to each of the four areas and I came up with a ranking of the researched countries. The pilot was done for 10 countries. Why these 10 countries? The countries are scattered around the globe as I wanted to make sure that my students had no bias in selecting those countries.

So, what I did was drafting the data collection sheet. I will try to illustrate the fact that on the left column I indicated the four areas of activities: assisted reproduction and fertility, research with embryos and stem cells, end-of-life decisions, and abortion and contraception. For each of the four areas, I listed questions that are important to understand freedom in each of these areas. For instance, the questions for assisted reproduction revolve around diagnosis, use of, ability to acquire and preserve (to put in refrigerator) reproductive tissue, donation of eggs and sperm, and surrogate agreements, that is agreements whereby people are able to have children on behalf of other individuals. In the second part, the third column on the document, the various questions are listed: is it permissible? If something is forbidden, you get 5 points. If it is free, you get 0.

For instance, for the third question, the one on the fourth column, are there limiting conditions?, if the answer is yes, you end up with a score between 1 and 4. The law in Italy prescribes limitations of what you can and cannot do. Many activities are not entirely forbidden, but some things are prohibited. The result is probably a score between 3 and 4, on the higher end. And so forth.

The question for conservation - "can a woman do cryopreserve eggs for future insemination? Preservation of sperm? Is donation of eggs or sperm permitted?" and so on - all these questions were asked for all areas and all countries. The column on the right reports the points. You have your points. You put them together, calculate the total, and the sum will be the overall degree of freedom of those countries, which have established different legal environments. So, my students collected the data through interviews with people, by looking up the internet, reading normative documents and legislation, occasionally legal opinions. They put together the points, I did the balancing - 25% to each area of study - and this is what we came up with. Again, I do not pretend it to be anything more informative than it was a study and this was the conclusion of the pilot. This is the ranking.

Based on the ranking, I tried to figure out some of the explanations of why certain countries are in certain positions. This could be an exercise in prejudices or a fine tuned analysis. At this stage, we are somewhere in between based on our intuitions of the various countries, some of which were not confirmed.

What should we look at, at this point, is the difference among European countries. We all come from an homogeneous tradition, based on certain degree of welfare system for citizens, basic constitutional frameworks. Yet, we score differently. If you look behind that, if you try to look at the society in which the legal frameworks are implemented, you start to understand that, for instance, there is a difference between Scandinavian countries and Ireland and Spain. Spain is part of the Mediterranean, influenced by the Catholic tradition. Ireland as well is very much influenced by the Catholic tradition. Once you start looking at the context of the policies, you begin to find patterns explaining the position of the various countries on the ranking chart. Since half of the study was about euthanasia and abortion, it makes a big difference, and Spain and Ireland are impacted by that. For instance, at this conference we had the Health Minister of Spain. I am not familiar with the details of stem cells research in Spain but the country ranks as rather conservative according to the study we did. Sweden is much more progressive in its social policies, hence the lowest score.

Panama is an interesting case. It scores very low. What is the explanation? The explanation is very simple. In some areas, such as embryonic stem cells, there is no legislation. If there is no legislation, there are no restrictions. That is an assumption, which may prove to be not true. But it shows that here we have a challenge: what is that we do with countries, that do not have regulation. The question is ultimately about capacity to do research and how it affects freedom. The role of the Muslim world and the discussion about Latin America in the global arena and its desire to be part of it depending on the benefits are important questions that may explain why countries are in a certain position. Political questions are relevant too as they can tell you a lot where countries are based on their commitments to certain international frameworks, their capacity to conduct research, and their social policies.

So, given the fact that we were able to find interesting data and patterns, I believe that monitoring is possible but it also requires collaborations and funding. At this stage, one of the challenges is still to find the right methodology and to improve it. Then, if we decide to run the study, we must expand it in terms of areas of human activity and countries. If we did that, we will have something interesting to contribute to the debate as policy-makers often learn from what others are doing as they realize that the problems are common and the range of solutions is limited.

Measuring freedom in relation to other countries, to similar democracies, is a good way of thinking about what we do as a country. In Italy for instance, we are very much aware of the fact that we are behind the rest of Europe. It is important for any country to realize where it positions itself in terms of the global arena.

Again there are huge challenges and it would be nice to have people collecting some of the data and acting as reviewers for their own countries. Ultimately, our plan is to write a couple of pages for each country summarizing what the status is there. We need people who are familiar with the context. We need money. I do not know if people in the room are able to solve it. Also, a lot has been published. For instance, the European Union contributed with a study that Marco passed me along, containing good legislative data. There is data out there and it is a matter of compiling it and using it.

Another question in measuring freedom is concerned with the overall question of the role of regulation itself. What if there is no regulation? What if regulation is not followed by people in the practice? You can only do it by talking to people and understanding what it means. In the UK, regulation is a good thing as it means that regulated activities are permitted. You can go on and do it. Regulation can be a very powerful instrument, not always a restriction of freedom. Also, among legal scholars, there is a longstanding debate on the differences between what we call the law in books and law in action. If you measure the conditions under which people act, the question and what is going on for real as opposed to what is that the law in the books says is relevant. Brazil makes stronger claims. It is my understanding that the degree of availability of abortion treatment in Brazil is really much higher than what the law allows people to do. The law is more restrictive than the practice. We ought to take that into account. Practices are important, perhaps as important as the framework. That is another part of the process to figure out how to account for the gap between restrictions in the law and reality.

Funding also is a big important component in measuring freedom. You may be able to do things, but you cannot because you do not have money. The ability to have funding is important in transforming opportunities into actions. One way to deal with this from a methodological standpoint is to add points to countries that do not have the (financial) capacity to do things, as you add points where researchers are not in the position to do certain things. It is necessary therefore to examine countries where funding is limited, such as in Africa where several healthcare systems are struggling with communicable diseases such as TB, HIV/AIDS and malaria, and where you will not find researchers engaged in fine-tuning stem cells research. This is a question of balancing. Again, points must be added. For instance, 5 points could be added to account for the absence of capacity to do research.

Finally, the talk on the Muslim world was revealing as it showed that the Muslim world is so far behind the scientific debate. It is clearly a political issue, and the report must discuss and highlight the political context in which medical research and practice operate - in this case of limited ability to act freely and participate in the debate because of the limited role that women play and the limiting social role played by families. It can be more of a political discussion. Also technological barriers, such as not having software to write in Islamic languages, must be accounted for.

Overall, I think the message is an optimistic one. The project is exciting and challenging. It will be interesting to put together our brains and think about it, to generate an international discussion through the permanent structure hosted by Luca Coscioni Association, which will deal with the implementation of the study. I am very much supportive of this project and we will find a way to complete it. Thanks for the opportunity to talk here.

*Assistant Professor of Legal Studies,
Department of History and Social Science,
Bryant University, USA

Marco Traub*
**Potential impact of advances in stem cell-based therapies
for Africa in the course of knowledge transfer
and affordable medicine**

My talk will focus on the socio-economic impact of freedom of science globally and pick up the context as presented before. I will describe in brief a project that I was made in charge of by the University
of Geneva in the course of constructing a center of excellence for regenerative medicine within a clinic project in Dakar, Senegal. I decided to include partners of my Trans-European Stem Cell Therapy
Consortium (TESCT).

First, I would like to explain in brief where I am coming from. My
research work is strongly funded by Johnson and Johnson and
Janssen Research Foundation, looking at human brain mapping and
pharmacology of opioid receptors with cloning and sequencing. I
had set up an entrepreneurship within the biotech area and was
teaching and coordinating research projects at the medical school
in Kansas City in the position of an assistant professor. Then I was
lucky enough to get funded by the European Commission and Swiss
government for several projects on developing state of the art technology in the area of xenotransplantation and reverse transcriptase-
polymerase chain reaction. It was a logical step to move into the field
of stem cells. Most recently, I am involved in structuring and building up the European stem cell consortium as well the related stem
cell foundation. I just would like to give a brief introduction on the
background of the stem cell consortium and to introduce its major
goal. The consortium mission is focused on encouraging transla-
tional research on stem cells for different clinical applications.

What is new in this foundation, as there are competing consortia
out there? It is the implementation of the patients' view. The patients'
and ethical view should not be peripheral - it will be centered. I am
encouraged by a number of stakeholders, i.e. from patient organizations and clinical researchers such as Mary Baker, the president
of the European Federation of Neurological Associations, along with
Stephen Minger, Julia Polak and Shimon Slavin. Just to give a brief
overview, our foundation board tries to incorporate the most excellent clinical researchers for embryonic as well adult stem cell expres-

sion profiling, in vivo imaging, disease models etc. So, this illustrates the approach, which is really focused on translation of research data to the patient. The patient is centered here as described before. As well I would like to shift to the economic impact of stem cell research, which is focused on the possibility of exploiting data as well knowledge management. But, based on the foundation, we want to make sure that we are also given free international access to collected data and knowledge, which are the results of the foundation work. This is a different approach, differing from the classical way of protecting knowledge as quickly as possible and transferring it to the market. Why Africa? As mentioned before the people of the University of Geneva set me in charge of setting up a department of regenerative medicine for a hospital that is planned at Dakar. Last week, our consortium had the chance in Dakar to present our view on stem cell research, application and implication for this kind of project. So, for example, we presented prominent clinical researchers like Stephen Minger from King's College, technology-related colleagues, as well speakers who are related to education. The approach, which was offered from University of Geneva to the President of Senegal, was basically anti-aging medicine in coordination with robotic and further state-of-the-art treatment for cancer. This raises ethical questions in the consortium. We immediately tried to set up a proposal for this kind of clinic project, which is estimated at a 200 million euro value. Our goal, also in an ethical perspective, is to focus on stem cell therapies and to support the implementation of the technology by education for sustained usage combined with knowledge transfer. And so, this would provide the medical centers and school in Dakar a possibility for sustained usage and further development. To date there is none or nearly no social healthcare infrastructure. Responsible people at the medical school welcomed this a kind of center of excellence. Now we are trying to setup single contracts where the international experts are invited and have a chance to educate the doctors and researchers in the country. We have clearly defined project ideas, which can be developed for the future. Here are some examples: from Stephen Minger from King's College on embryonic stem cells to Thomas Ekström from the Karolinska Institute on epigenetic profiling. From that point of view, the major problem for us was to understand, what the official side is really interested in. We got a clear message that a center of excellence for Africa with technology transfer is one of the major needs. Additionally we tried to understand what is the need of the average person in Senegal. Do the people need robotic surgery on the heart or rather simplified stem cell application offering a cheaper possibility to get access to advanced technology? There is no clear answer yet. Stem cells do not offer a real cure up to now. But it is very clear all over Europe and the United States that adult stem cells are used for treatment of heart failure, diabetic leg and arthritis. It would make sense to seriously consider this kind of technology as a possible technology for the African countries, as it is less expensive and the handling of certain applications is unsophisticated. From that point of view, we tried to find out what we can do under these circumstances for the average person with a life expectancy of 60. Does it make sense to construct such kind of center for the elite? On the other hand, we have to be careful. If this is the desire of the president, we have to not start criticizing because we are trying to avoid being suspected as neo-colonialists. So, are anti-aging treatment, such as laser and cosmetics, offering a solution for the people living in the street? We learned that only 30,000 people out of millions are able to pay for that kind of treatment. We elucidated that one of the major healthcare problems is diabetes and obesity, which is astonishing for an African country. We are proposing the influence of virus infection.

We think that any kind of change in the infrastructure of the healthcare system should be based on knowledge and education. This will really have a strong sociological impact on this kind of African countries.

Finally I would like to present and thank my consortium team for sustained support: Stephen Minger, King's College; Rosie Graham, Stem Cell Foundation; Thomas Ekström, Karolinska Institute; Miomir Knecevic, BTC; Shimon Slavin, Nissim Benvenisty; Yoav Mayshar; Julia Polak; Kishore Bhakoo; Andreas Junge.

*TESCT - Transeuropean Stem Cell Therapy Consortium,
Switzerland and United Kingdom

Willy De Greef*
Bioscience, biotechnology and social value

I am going to give the audience a view on where science clashes with society from the perspective of people who use science to develop things that are going to reach society as a product or service or information to support policy-making or implementation.

When you take value-free science and start using it to solve problems, you run into conflicts. It is going to interact with values and belief systems. Often the interaction tends to be conflictual. The industry sectors I represent interact more than most sectors with these value systems. We work with stem cells, with genetic engineering, with nanotechnology. We push every button where people say: do I want this or the product of science? That is because our sectors touch on what people are, their bodies, what they eat, the environment they live in. So it is not surprising that occasionally you get hard questions.

A good example is how the revolution in genetics is changing the way we treat disease. Until a few years ago, I would say 90% of the biomedical technology budget and attention was on treatments, pharmaceutical products, radiation etc. Today however, by far the fastest growing area of biomedical science is diagnostics. For example we know there is no such thing as breast cancer. There are a dozen diseases we put under that common name. The reason why there is no general treatment is that all the treatments are for particular kinds of breast cancer, but those were recognizable as separate diseases thanks to the revolution in diagnostics. It is completely changing the way we use medical science, and it has consequences for future healthcare policies.

So when you start using science to provide products through technology, you have to assume you will see some conflict with belief systems. There is no alternative for being pro-active in approaching this situation, because those whose belief systems you will touch are going to try to use their power in politics and society, not only to stop you from bringing products to the table or to the patient in the clinic, but they will probably try to stop you earlier, during the R&D phase.

For example, a couple of months ago a South African NGO funded by an European NGO, tried to stop a German boat that was going to do an ocean fertilising experiment by leaving the harbor of Cape Town. The reason is: in climate change, the biggest challenge for society, there is a deep gap between those who see science and technology as part of the solution and those who see science and technology as the problem.

People whose belief system proclaims that science is a part of the problem will try to stop science very early on. That is something that comes very close to repudiating the freedom of fundamental research. But it mostly works by making it impossible to use science to test solutions to practical problems before you implement them in policy.

Another case is protection of biodiversity. Much of it has to do with the way we position the need to protect biodiversity and the way we deal with it. Protecting and transferring biodiversity to future generations is a moral duty, just like transferring our cultural heritage. These are moral goods - they are priceless. But protecting them has a cost. If you want to protect them effectively, then you have a duty also to manage your resources allocated to this in a cost-efficient way so as to achieve the maximum amount of result with the resources available. However, most policies directed at protection of biodiversity work the way round: they justify the need for protection on economic grounds, and then become very picky about which science and technology will be used in the actual management of the effort.

How did we get that way? Those of us who work on the interface between science and policy know that one of the biggest problems is scientific illiteracy, which is getting worse. Partly this comes from the way we teach science to children, which often looks like a deliberate attempt to make it as boring and as irrelevant as possible. Result is, when they are 18-19 and have to go to university, they do not choose life sciences. Sooner or later they will be members of parliament, ministers, and their only memory about science will be of something difficult and boring.

We need to use all available means to find ways to make science fun again, not only to young people, but also old people. One of the biggest services we can do to increase acceptance of scientific freedom, is to start very early on in science education and work harder on giving people continuous education about science. That opens their minds. And that allows them to see science as something that they can think critically about, that is part of their world.

*Secretary General,
EuropaBio - European Association for Bioindustries

Marco Pannella*
Conclusions

I feel that the first thing required is that I make a brief comment about our strength and the serious limitations of our situation. There are also, of course, some more amusing aspects, also thanks to another Marco, one of the several Marcos who have spoken at the Congress, three of whom are radicals and share the same approach and who, albeit with huge generational differences, live and fight on together.

The venue in which we are holding our meeting is a venue in which we are able to meet because Marco Cappato and I are here, for the moment, in the European Parliament, hence we have made use of one of the prerogatives we are granted as Members of the European Parliament, with the solid support of the liberal group and also the presence and backing of the socialist group. This is a fact which we are keen to highlight, if only because it does not happen often and because I believe we should all hope that it should happen in the future that socialists, as well as nationalists and any other varieties which may be present in the Parliament, might find themselves increasingly interested in supporting this initiative of ours.

I had misunderstood the task entrusted to me, that of drawing conclusions from this morning's debate togheter with Busquin. At any rate, I found it impossible to follow this morning's discussion, with the exception of the last part. I would like to take advantage of this opportunity to speak, not to present an overview of the progress of the congress, but to add a few themes which I feel were barely touched on in the presentations, and in our lives in general.

Keeping company with the Dalai Lama and the Tibetan Buddhists, myself and Marco Cappato discovered to our surprise that the phenomenon of Tibetan religious feeling could be a very important support for we secularists, seen as believers and non-believers, in conventional and traditional terms. I think we are a good way along the road to the conviction that the secular condition is also the condition highlighted in the religions revealed by the Revealer. It is in fact a characteristic of Christianity, for example, that God wished to involve himself in human history, so emphasising the way in which the relationship of the divine absolute with humanity can be seen as that with the individual conscience, with personal existence. From that point of view, believing also means believing in one's enormous responsibility and freedom which requires no intermediary to ask questions or receive replies from the mystery of the transcendent or other mysteries. We should encourage a greater presence of the Tibetans, a challenge we are currently dealing with. Paying a visit, also quite recently, in company with Matteo Mecacci, to the Tibetan museums, such as that concerned with astronomy, in reality the history of medicine, we witnessed some extraordinary phenomena and a philosophical dimension, a cognitive dimension, inspired by the infinite, the eternal. Hence when you ask how many Buddhas there are, you are told that the number is infinite, because there is a Buddha for all times.

From the point of view of freedom of research, the Dalai Lama himself has recently confirmed the fact that where there are persistent differences between scriptural truths - in Buddhism, the scriptures are written by writers, speaking on their own behalf, not on behalf of God, and are sustainable truths as far as science is concerned -, they and their interpretations need to be updated, to remain in keeping with research, which is seen as researching into the infinite.

When the Dalai Lama recently came to Venice, he was questioned about the Englaro case, that of the Italian woman who had been in a vegetative state for 17 years, and he confirmed that life must always be respected. The newspaper headlines claimed: "The Dalai Lama agrees with the Pope". What the Dalai Lama actually said was that this was true for life in general, but specified that life must be valued on a case-by-case basis. No one here would wish to impose the rule of passive euthanasia. Marco Cappato, with Matteo Mecacci and some Tibetan Buddhist intellectuals, are striving to develop initiatives which could lead to some form of enrichment, which is tremendously urgent for other forms of religious sentiment. We "Marcos", as Italians, find ourselves faced with the problem of the new papacy which is not fond of us because we are regarded, according papacy to a confirmed and widespread definition, as "those who support the choice of death", while on the other side there are those who "support the choice of life". We are deemed to be responsible for the holocaust of the embryos, as a cardinal put it the other day, stating that every generation is responsible for the holocaust of 100,000 embryos.

A considerable number of us, including Marco Cappato, Emma Bonino and myself, worked to organise the meeting in Turkey and we have spoken with Erdogan about this.

At present, ongoing productive activity is under way as a part of this Congress. For example, Venice, March 7: "New hopes of the possibility of extracting substances from amniotic fluid to be used in disease treatments". We can already imagine the reactions to the possibility of using adult stem cells, or the other kind, those which are not actually adult as they are manufactured chemically. Dr. Massimiliano Manganini, together with the Scientific Director of the Cellular Center, assures us that "this research into amniotic fluid represents a step forward for research because of the high differentiation and proliferation level, as well as the fact that they have no implications from the ethical point of view, which is more important". There the most important thing is that there are no implications from the ethical point of view, which so assumes the existence of a single authority in charge of ethics, a State, one with which we must be increasingly concerned to settle our accounts.

We recently heard the news of the solemn, publicised, excommunication (seen as the height of indignity and infamy) of some doctors, nurses and hospital workers who performed an abortion on a nine-year-old child who had been a rape victim at the age of eight. In the time of the Inquisition, those who wished to perform research on corpses or autopsies were burned at the stake.

The next Congress will be helped by this Congress, an attitude I fully support. In the meantime, I trust that we shall together be able to undertake some research into the demographic problem. When we try to defend the responsibility for the freedom of the individual, of belief, in response to which people go back to saying that it should be "natural", hostile reactions are provoked. I wonder if it may be that the human species is passing through a conflict-ridden phase. On the one hand it is as though we were witnessing a resurrection of the extreme and ancient anthropological strength of the species, whereby reproduction was a symbol of power and essential to survival, which now defends, in an almost fetishist and obsessive way, the non-dispersal of the seed, of the stem cells – while on the other, we are the species which places the importance on procreating with love rather than breeding like animals. Their materialism is so coarse as to be an offence against materialism itself. According to them, all it wants is that second of coming together for the person to exist, and woe betide those who doubt that. This is fetishist worship, which adores the embryo or the zygote which cannot even be seen through a microscope, as it does the human body, better because it is a blank, which has lain there for 17 years, incapable of sin, incapable of evil, which even if it does not wish to, is obliged to live, if it can be called life, while, at the statistical level, 50,000 or 60,000 humans died that night or the day before, in other parts of the world, with other histories. On this matter I feel we must give a brave answer, on the effect of human action on natural environments and the "mild return" [to a world with two billion people] but certainly with regard to a human species able to contribute to a happy and positive future for nature, which is a story rather than a place.

So this is my wish, and not the summary, because I have no right to allocate that to anyone. Thank you, Marco.

*Member of the European Parliament; leader of the Nonviolent Radical Party

Programme and list of participants

1ST DAY – THURSDAY, MARCH 5TH

Opening Ceremony

- Marco Cappato, MEP; Secretary General, Luca Coscioni Association
- Janez Potočnik, European Commissioner for Science and Research
- Charles Sabine, NBC News Correspondent
- Kary Mullis, Nobel Prize in Chemistry, 1993, "Scientific progress is a rocky road"
- Philippe Busquin, MEP; former Commissioner for Science and Research

1st session:
Past and future of scientific freedom

- Elena Cattaneo, Director, Centre for Stem Cell Research, University of Milan, Italy; Coordinator of NeuroStemCell Consortium
- Emma Bonino, Vice-President, Italian Senate; former European Commissioner
- Bernat Soria, Minister of Health, Spain
- Gilberto Corbellini, History of Medicine and Bioethics, University of Rome "Sapienza", Italy; Co-President, Luca Coscioni Association, "Retrospectives and prospects on the freedom of science from the viewpoint of a historian"
- Graham Watson, President, ALDE group

2nd session:
The ethical, political and legal foundation
of freedom of research and teaching

- John Harris, Bioethics, University of Manchester, United Kingdom, "Taking the "human" out of human rights and the "dignity" out of human dignity and putting the science back"
- Dick Taverne, founder, Sense about Science; Member, House of

Lords Science and Technology Committee, United Kingdom, "Freedom of research and eco-fundamentalism"
• Mark B. Brown, Research Associate, Bielefeld Graduate School in History and Sociology, Bielefeld University, Germany, "What does it mean to have a right to research?"
• Barbara Forrest, Department of History & Political Science, Southeastern Louisiana University, USA, "Restoring the Enlightenment: the foundation of American and European science and education"
• Amedeo Santosuosso, Judge, Milan Court of Appeal, Italy, "May scientific research work as a model for present transnational law?"

2ND DAY – FRIDAY, MARCH 6TH

• Audrey Simpson, Director, Family Planning Association, Northern Ireland, "The legal, political and social context of the provision of abortion services in Northern Ireland"
• Laurence Bovy on behalf of Laurette Onkelinx, Minister of Health, Belgium

Session proposed by
ESHRE - European Society of Human Reproduction:
"The challenges for reproductive medicine in Europe"

• Anna Veiga, Spain, "Reproductive medicine and stem cells"
• Lone Schmidt, Denmark, "Reproduction and the population crisis"
• Joep Geraedts, ESHRE Chairman, The Netherlands, "Genetics and reproductive health"
• Luca Gianaroli, ESHRE Chairman elect, Italy, "Assisted reproduction in Europe"
• Paul de Vroey, Belgium, "Healthy babies and safe treatments"

3rd session:
The religious, bioethical and political approaches
to freedom of research

• Marco Pannella, MEP; leader of the Nonviolent Radical Party
• Alex Mauron, Associate Professor of Bioethics, University of Geneva Medical School, Switzerland, "Epistemological relativism and religious dogma: two strange bedfellows in the struggle against freedom of scientific research"
• Pervez Hoodbhoy, Chairman, Department of Physics, Quaid-e-Azam University, Pakistan, "The battle for science and secularism in the Islamic world"

4th session:
The geopolicy and the future of genetic,
regenerative and reproductive medicine

- Giulio Cossu, Director, Stem Cell Research Institute Dibit, H. San Raffaele, Italy, "The new therapies ahead: promises, challenges and risks"
- Miguel Kottow, Universidad de Chile; Member, Latin American and Caribbean Network for Bioethics of UNESCO, "Why the Third World needs its own view on science"
- Stephen Minger, Director, King's Stem Cell Biology Laboratory, London, "Therapeutic and research potential of human pluripotent stem cells"

Roundtable:
"Neuroethics: challenges and opportunities"

- Piergiorgio Strata, Scientific Director, European Brain Research Institute; Co-President, Luca Coscioni Association
- Kathinka Evers, Center for Research Ethics and Bioethics, Uppsala, Sweden, "Towards a philosophy for neuroethics: informed materialism and the naturalistic responsibility"
- Eric Racine, Director, Neuroethics Research Unit, Institut de recherches cliniques, Montréal, Canada, "Neuroethics: tackling the ethical and social challenges of the neuroscience revolution"

3RD DAY – SATURDAY, MARCH 7TH

5th session:
Freedom of research between funding, careers and politics

- Gabriela Gebrin Cezar, Assistant Professor, University of Wisconsin-Madison, USA, "Freedom of scientific research as a vehicle for social and economic transformation"
- Piergiorgio Strata
- Martin L. Perl, Nobel Prize in Physics, 1995, "Limitations on research and development in science and technology"
- Josè Mariano Gago, Minister for Science and Technology, Portugal

Conclusions:
The way ahead: the globlal monitoring on the state of freedom
of research and other missions for a permanent World Congress

- Marco Cappato
- Andrea Boggio, Assistant Professor of Legal Studies, Department of History and Social Science, Bryant University, USA, "Freedom of research around the globe: a preliminary study"
- Marco Traub, Transeuropean Stem Cell Therapy Consortium (TESCT), Switzerland and United Kingdom, "Potential impact of advances in stem cell-based therapies for Africa in the course of knowledge transfer and affordable medicine"
- Willy De Greef, Secretary General, EuropaBio - European Association for Bioindustries
- Marco Pannella

With the participation of:
- Alfredo Aguilar, Head of Biotechnology Unit , Directorate Food, Agriculture and Biotechnology, DG Research, European Commission
- Ofra Balaban, President, CHEN Patient Fertility Association, Israel
- John Bowis, Member of the European Parliament, EPP Group
- Chemsi Chéref-Khan, President, European Institute of Muslim Humanism
- Moncif Cherkaoui, Morocco Embassy Counsellor
- Stefan Cibian, DG Development and Relation with African, Caribbean and Pacific States, European Commission
- Giovanna Corda, MEP, Socialist Group
- Evy Reviers, Director, ALS Liga, Belgium
- Antonino Forabosco, Medical Genetics, University of Modena and Reggio Emilia, Italy
- Filomena Gallo, President, "Amica Cicogna" ONLUS and Vice-Secretary, Luca Coscioni Association
- Simona Giordano, University of Manchester, UK
- Sabine Henry, Chairman, Ligue Alzheimer ASBL
- James Hougthon, Professor, University of Galway
- Marisa Jaconi, Department of Pathology and Immunology, Geneva University, Switzerland
- Dainis Krievins, Head of the Education and Science Department of the Pauls Stradins Clinical University Hospital, Riga Latvia
- Mihail Kritikos, Ethics and Governance Unit, Ethics Review, Sector DG Research, European Commission
- Philippe Mahoux, Senator and President of the Socialist Group in the Senate, Belgium
- Gerhard Maynhardt, Minister Plenipotentiary at the Austrian Embassy in Brussels
- Christian Mirre, Scientology
- Barletta Nottebohm, Panama Embassy Counsellor

- Vladko Panayotov, MEP, ALDE Group
- Neil Parish, MEP, EPP Group
- Sandra Pinto Marquez, Scientific Officer DG Research, Genomics and Systems Biology, European Commission
- Jean-Paul Pirnay, Burn Centre Military Hospital, Brussels
- John Purvis, MEP, EPP Group
- Rui Reis, University of Minho, Portugal
- Altagracia Reyes, Domenican Republic Embassy
- Danny Reviers, ALS Liga Belgium
- Aloyzan Sakalas, MEP, Socialist Group
- Wilhelmine Schett, Luca Coscioni Association
- Maurilio Sampaolesi, Assistant Professor, University of Leuven
- Gabriela Schneider, Kommissariat der Deutschen Bischöfe, Berlin, Germany
- Loana Siska, DG Research, Health Research, European Commission
- Peter Stastny, MEP, EPP Group
- Urbano Stenta, Foreign Affairs Ministry, Italy
- Mohammed Soumani, Algerian Mission to Brussels, Scientific Research Issues
- Giuseppe Tritto, Executive Chairman, World Academy of Biomedical Sciences and Technologies (UNESCO)
- Marc Van Montagu, Chairman, EFB - European Federation of Biotechnology
- Gilbert Verbeken, Burn Centre Military Hospital, Brussels
- Catherine Verfaillie, Director, Interdepartementaal Stamcelinstituut, University of Leuven